The Story of
WEATHER

Bill Giles

The Met Office

The Story of
WEATHER

Produced in association with Shell U.K. Limited

London: HMSO

Devised by Complete Editions
Designed by Craig Dodd
Maps by Terry Brown

A list of Shell publications can be obtained by writing to:
Department UKPA/146
Shell UK Ltd
PO Box No. 148
Shell-Mex House
Strand
London WC2R 0DX

HMSO publications are available from:

HMSO Publications Centre
(Mail and telephone orders only)
PO Box 276, London, SW8 5DT
Telephone orders 071-873 9090
General enquiries 071-873 0011
(queuing system in operation for both numbers)

HMSO Bookshops
49 High Holborn, London, WC1Q 6HB   071-873 0011 (Counter service only)
258 Broad Street, Birmingham, B1 2HE   021-643 3740
Southey House, 33 Wine Street, Bristol, BS1 2BQ   (0272) 264306
9-21 Princess Street, Manchester, M60 8AS   061-834 7201
80 Chichester Street, Belfast, BT1 4JY   (0232) 238451
71 Lothian Road, Edinburgh, EH3 9AZ   031-228 4181

HMSO's Accredited Agents
(see Yellow Pages)

And through good booksellers

Contents

Introduction

My interest in meteorology began at an early age. I hated wet Fridays at my boarding school in Crediton, Devon. The choice was between going for an aimless cross-country run or joining a club. The geography club had a Stephenson Screen and, as well as making weather observations, members got their first insight into forecasting the weather–so I joined. Once you get hooked on the weather it becomes an all-consuming interest, and what better way to indulge yourself than to join the Meteorological Office and do it full-time?

In the 1960s, as an observer for the Meteorological Office, I travelled all over the world and spent four months on Christmas Island in the South Pacific during the last of the nuclear bomb tests. However, after a while just observing the weather, even tracking huge hydrogen balloons into the high atmosphere, can become a little boring; so I decided to study and become a forecaster.

Having progressed to an instructor at the Meteorological Office Training School, I went underground to the RAF HQ at Strike Command, High Wycombe. In the meantime, as all students did, I had a voice test and was accepted as having potential to broadcast.

My chance eventually came in 1972 when auditions were held at the London Weather Centre for a vacancy on the national radio team, broadcasting the weather forecast on BBC radio. The consequence of not getting the job was to be put into an administrative post at High Wycombe. . . so I tried extra hard and was given the broadcasting job.

I duly arrived at the London Weather Centre in November 1972 and only then realized that the job of a weather forecaster at a weather centre is totally different to that of forecasting anywhere else, because the language is so different. Within meteorology, as in most scientific disciplines, we use a shorthand language or jargon when talking to one another, whereas the job of a forecaster in a weather centre is to talk to the general public in the language they understand. In other words, a forecaster must be able to translate the jargon into everyday language.

Some of this jargon concerns showers. For instance, there are isolated showers, scattered showers and occasional showers, all meaning something different. Isolated showers means a 10 per cent chance of catching one; scattered showers a 30 per cent chance; and occasional showers a 50 per cent chance, if you stay in the same place. But of course, most people we are broadcasting to do not know that, so the broadcaster's job is simply to convey to the listeners the chances of getting wet – or staying dry.

There are many things the broadcaster has to bear in mind, for example, when forecasting thunderstorms. I am conscious that many people are afraid of them. I remember one dear lady told me she hated them so much that whenever we forecast a storm she went under the stairs with a bottle of gin. . . but as she was now diabetic she could not take the gin! So now I only mention them when I am quite sure they will occur.

One day in 1975 I noticed a 'T' on my roster and asked my boss what it meant. He said that it meant I was to go for a television audition at the BBC. I got the job. I only recently found out why: while the only other serious contender was auditioning the clock stopped, and by the time it was set going again he had only two seconds of the broadcast to forecast tomorrow's weather. He smiled sweetly and said: 'Tomorrow's weather will be similar'. . .

I worked under Jack Scott for the next five years using the magnetic symbols once so familiar on our television forecasts, then got promoted and went to the Meteorological Office headquarters at Bracknell. I came back to television in 1983 in charge of the BBC team, and introduced the new electronic weather system two years later.

The television forecaster is governed by time. Each broadcast has to finish exactly on the second because there is an eight-second time delay, and eight seconds before our broadcast ends

Bill Giles.

the next programme starts to run – and cannot be stopped. So if you are two seconds early you stand, or sit, and grin like a Cheshire Cat, or, as I do, keep winking until the time runs out! At the BBC we are a one-man or one-woman band: weather expert, producer, director and presenter all rolled into one, going out live with no script written for us. There is, however, enormous support from the parent organization, the Meteorological Office. We have conferences with Bracknell several times a day, when the senior forecaster briefs us on the likely weather trends. There are twice-daily data transmissions, plus hourly satellite pictures and half-hourly rainfall radar pictures. Using this bank of statistics and information we draw the electronic charts to tell the weather story for the next broadcast.

We actually broadcast nineteen times on an average weekday, each broadcast varying in length from fifteen seconds to three and a half minutes. Once the maps are ready, the weather bulletin mapped out, and their faces powdered, the television weather broadcasters are ready to broadcast and the adrenalin starts to flow quickly. It is a far cry from getting out of a two-mile run on a wet Friday in Devon thirty years ago!

What is Weather?

The weather is such a fundamental part of our lives yet very often we take it for granted. Perhaps, because weather is around us all the time, in the form of rain, sun, snow, wind or frost we only take notice of it when something out of the ordinary happens, such as exceptional winds or a drought.

In recent years, however, the weather and what causes it have become increasingly popular topics and the subject of many newspaper articles and television programmes. The reason for this, of course, is not hard to see. A growing worldwide awareness of the environment has made mankind realize that we can, and do, have a major impact on the weather around us – for good or for bad. Of particular concern have been the so-called greenhouse effect and the feared thinning of the atmosphere's ozone layer, both of which may have a significant and harmful impact on the Earth's climate, as I discuss in the final chapter.

The global conditions that govern the weather as it is now are no longer the preserve of the sciences of meteorology and climatology; they now form a discussion point up and down the country. Recent extremes of weather in Britain, such as the 'hurricane' of 1987, the winds and floods of early 1990 and the severe droughts of 1976 and 1989 have rammed home the message that the weather cannot be taken for granted and may indeed be changing. In fact, if we look back at the world's weather hundreds of thousands, if not millions, of years ago we can see that the Earth's climate is constantly changing and fluctuating on patterns occurring over the long, medium and short term. What can appear 'normal' on the human scale of time may be nothing more than a mere aberration set against the vastness of time.

Weather is defined in the *Concise Oxford Dictionary* as 'Atmospheric conditions prevailing at a time and place, combination produced by heat or cold, clearness or cloudiness, dryness or moisture, wind or calm, high or low pressure, and electrical state, of local air and sky.' The origins of the word 'weather' are Old English or Norse and may have roots in an old Germanic word for 'to blow' as in the wind – appropriately enough as it is the wind which helps shape and bring much of our weather.

The word is common and familiar enough to have crept into various expressions such as someone feeling 'under the weather' meaning poorly, or someone making 'heavy weather' of a job or task. You will also sometimes hear people refer to a day when there was 'no weather'. Strictly speaking this is not true as even the most perfect or bland conditions are weather (it is something always with us), but in this sense the word is used to mean there was no rain or snow.

Since the dawn of time man has relied on the weather to survive. It is true to say that without the weather systems, which distribute rain and winds around the globe, maintaining habitable living conditions, there could be no life on Earth. However, weather 'the provider' can also be weather 'the destroyer', for example, the monsoon rains which affect areas of Asia, as well as other parts of the world. These torrential rains bring the essential moisture to nourish crops which keep vast numbers of people alive, but they can also bring floods, destruction and, on occasions, death.

In early times the weather was also important. For example, in the Bible there are references to floods and droughts, notably the Great Flood which only Noah and his family survived. In mythologies around the world and throughout recorded time there have been numerous gods of the weather. One of the most famous was Thor, the Germanic god of thunder. His power was said to be in his hammer, a thunderbolt, and he was reputedly one of the mightiest of the gods. One writer of the 12th century described him in this way: 'Thor, the mightiest of the three, stands in the centre of the building, with Wodan and Fricco on his right and left. Thor, they say, holds the dominion of the air. He rules over thunder and lightning, winds and rain, clear weather and fertility. When plague or famine threatens, sacrifice is offered to Thor.'

This passage displays the crucial importance that men attached to the weather. Another god of the weather was Boreas, the Greek god of the north wind, who helped damage the Persian fleet in the 5th century BC; while in East Africa there is the god, En-kai, the rain god of the Masai, who brings the life-giving rains that water the plains of their homeland.

Early man displayed other affinities with nature and the elements such as the extraordinary structure at Stonehenge, which, whatever its intended purpose, does show an awareness and alignment with the life-giving sun. Early hunters too were in tune with their surroundings and used to read the natural signals around them, for example keeping an eye on the migration of birds. In Europe, Iron Age man learnt to cope with conditions much colder than the present day while, as I describe later in the chapter on forecasting, in the east astrologers looked at the planets and stars to help them foretell such disasters as floods and earthquakes. Such large-scale climatic events were supposed to be omens, and for some they even heralded the *dies irae* (literally 'day of wrath'), the Last Judgement and the end of the world. As Calphurnia, Caesar's wife, says prophetically in Shakespeare's *Julius Caesar*, 'When beggars die there are no comets seen; The heavens themselves blaze forth the death of princes.'

Nearer to our own times, it was by mastering the winds, that essential part of the weather, that navigators from Europe were able to sail out and discover the so-called New World and develop trade routes, with a vital impact on the course of civilization. Indeed, the *trade winds* still retain their name from that era.

Away from the more practical aspects, it is the weather too that provides us with some of the most beautiful sights in the natural world: magnificent sunsets and sunrises, rainbows, the sun dispersing early morning mist and the changing of the seasons.

Having set the scene, then, I now want to move on to perhaps the most important single element of weather, without which nothing else could happen – the sun.

The Sun

Man has long worshipped the sun, and little wonder. As archeology shows us, the peoples of South and Central America, the ancient Greeks with their god, Helios, and many other early civilizations, appreciated that the sun is the driving force for everything that occurs on the Earth – its energy storehouse. Many millions of years ago it was the rays of the sun which first helped create life on the planet and without it we would be as lifeless as those distant planets in the solar system – Neptune, Uranus and Pluto – whose distance from the sun leaves them almost unimaginably cold.

It is the sun which provides the energy which drives our own weather system. The sun itself is a moderately small star in terms of the universe, some 1,392,000 kilometres (865,000 miles) in diameter. Even so it is many times greater than the size of Earth. The phenomenal energy it gives out comes from thermonuclear reactions occurring inside the heart of the globe, which give rise to temperatures of up to 6000°C (11000°F) on its surface.

The energy produced naturally travels in all directions from its surface and only a small part of this is intercepted by the Earth as it travels through space on its 365.25-day orbit around the sun. (It is this quarter day which gives rise to the leap year every four years, when an extra day is added to the month of February.)

Our orbit around the sun is not perfectly circular. It is what is called elliptical, that is oval-shaped. This means that the Earth's distance from the sun may vary throughout its orbit by as much as 4,800,000 kilometres (3,000,000 miles).

As it happens it is not the distance from the sun which determines the varying seasons we experience. In fact it is in January that the northern hemisphere is closest to the sun and in July that it is furthest away. The seasons are caused by a tilt in the Earth in relation to the plane in which it travels around the sun. This tilt, of 66.5° to the plane, is fixed throughout the orbit and it means that at different times of the year, first the northern hemisphere, and then the southern hemisphere, gets the most direct sunlight. This effect can perhaps best be imagined by visualizing what the situation would be if the Earth was exactly at right angles to the plane during the whole orbit. In this situation, the whole Earth would have twelve-hour days, except the unfortunate poles, and there would be no seasons anywhere. As it is, the northern and southern hemispheres are alternately 'thrust' into the most direct rays of the sun. Thus at the summer solstice in June in the north, the sun is directly above the Tropic of Cancer which lies at about latitude 23.5°N, while at the corresponding winter solstice in December the sun is directly above the Tropic of Capricorn at about latitude 23.5°S. It can be seen from this, then, that at both the March and September equinoxes, the sun is directly above the equator.

The Weather Machine

Having looked at a few facts about the sun, it is time to consider how it drives our weather systems or the planet's 'weather machine'. One might ask why, with the constant heating by the sun over many millions of years, the Earth does not increase in temperature and become hotter and hotter, rather like a glowing coal in a furnace. If this was to happen, of course, we would all have been burnt to a cinder a long time ago.

The answer is that the Earth both reflects and radiates heat itself. Around one-third of the sun's energy that reaches the top of the Earth's atmosphere is reflected directly back into space while the equivalent of the remaining two-thirds is radiated out by the surface of the Earth. This, incidentally, as we shall find in the last chapter lies at the crux of the debate on the greenhouse effect.

Although the different regions of the Earth receive similar amounts of sunlight, they do not receive similar amounts of heating. There are several reasons for this. The first, and crucial one, is the angle at which the sunlight hits the Earth. At the equator, where the sun is more or less directly overhead the whole year round, the angle is direct and the power of the sun's rays more concentrated. We have all experienced days in the sun when although the sun's light is the same, it is considerably hotter when the sun is above us. At the poles, in contrast, the angle at which the sunlight hits has the effect of diffusing the power of the rays. In addition, this angle forces the sun's rays to travel through a thicker layer of atmosphere which again reduces their intensity and power. A further factor is what is known as the 'albedo' of various surfaces. The albedo of a surface is the amount of sun radiation it reflects back. At the poles the ice and snow are both very effective reflectors of the heat, preventing the sun from raising the temperatures there. By contrast, the sand in a desert reflects only around one-quarter of the sun's heat. Water does not reflect much heat when the sun is above it, but in instances such as the Arctic Ocean, where the sun is at a low angle, it becomes a good reflector.

So you might wonder why, if the equator and tropics absorb so much of the Earth's incoming heat and the poles and higher latitudes so little, the equator does not get hotter and hotter and the Antarctic and the Arctic colder and colder. The reason they do not is because of heat transference to other parts of the planet. That is to say that the warmer air at the equator is moved around the rest of the world, bringing warmth to colder regions, not unlike a domestic heating system.

At its simplest this process would lead to a very straightforward circulation of winds around the Earth, making it relatively easy to understand weather patterns. Under this idealized model the warm air from the equatorial regions would rise up into the atmosphere, travel polewards gradually descending all the time until the air reached the poles. With this model we can see that at the equator the warmer air would create lower pressure, while at the poles the pressure would be higher

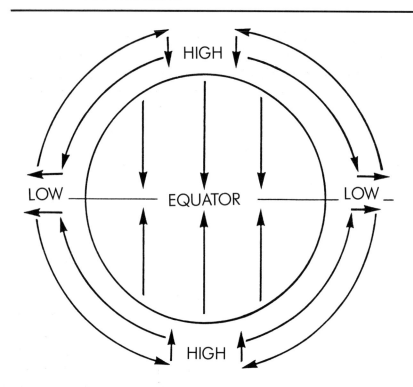

◀ Winds on a non-rotating globe

as the cooling, and thus denser, air descends upon it. This would then cause the colder air at the poles to move outwards back towards the equator and the lower pressure. A basic rule of meteorology is that air moves from high to low- pressure areas.

Such a view of the world was indeed put forward by an Englishman, George Hadley, in the mid-18th century to explain weather patterns. However, the theory fails to take into account one crucial factor – the rotation of the Earth. As we know, the Earth is constantly spinning on its axis, once every twenty-four hours, rather like a spinning ball. A person standing at the equator is thus travelling at about 1,600km/h (1,000mph) around that axis, although of course unaware of it. In contrast, anyone standing at the poles, through which the Earth's axis lies, would be motionless in relation to the spinning. At points in between the equator and the poles the speed of the rotation naturally varies between 1,600km/h (1,000mph) and nought.

Travelling polewards the winds themselves are subject to these variations which cause them to be 'dragged' to one side. This deflection of the winds by the Earth's rotation, causing those heading polewards in the northern hemisphere to deflect eastwards as westerlies, lies behind the complexity of our 'weather machine'. The spin of the Earth affecting the winds is known as the *Coriolis* effect or force. Another complicating factor is the presence of large land masses, especially mountain ranges, and massive oceans which produce different effects in the weather.

But the Hadley model is not entirely redundant, for in certain areas of the world this theory does in fact hold good. Such circulations are known as *Hadley cells*. One example is found over the equator where hot air rises, moves polewards and then descends at around latitudes 20° to 30° north and south. The descent of the air causes high pressure and relatively dry and stable weather. Many of the world's deserts, for example the Sahara in the northern hemisphere and the Atacama in the southern hemisphere, occur in this area. From these areas of high pressure, conforming to the Hadley model, winds flow back towards the equator where the 'cycle' is then repeated. These winds that flow back to the equator, however, do not flow in direct north-south or south-north lines because of the Coriolis effect. In the northern hemisphere they blow as north-easterlies (remember that winds are always described in terms of the direction from which they come), while in the southern hemisphere they blow as south-easterlies. These winds are fairly constant and strong and became known to sailors in the 18th century as trade winds because they helped carry merchant ships across the oceans. They assisted European sailors heading south-west across the mid-Atlantic.

These trade winds occur between the sub-tropics, where the tropical air is descending, and the equator itself. The area where they converge is known as the *Inter-Tropical Convergence Zone* (ITCZ). This zone can be viewed in effect as a kind of movable equator, or as the meteorological equator, as opposed to the geographical one which is fixed. The zone moves from north to south but is always close to the true equator. In general the ITCZ is in whichever hemisphere is experiencing summer.

With air converging on the zone, the ITCZ is generally an area where air is rising. As we shall learn elsewhere in the book, rising air containing moisture is a condition which creates rain and indeed the ITCZ is present over some of the wettest parts of the globe, the tropical rain forests of South America being one such area. Incidentally, in the South American country of Ecuador, the nation named after the equator, there is a monument a few miles north of the capital, Quito, marking the

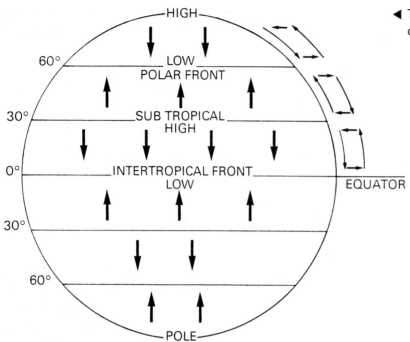

◀ Three-dimensional wind pattern on a non-rotating globe

spot through which the line of the equator runs. Logically, however, this is no more the 'middle of the world' than any other point on the equator's circumference of the Earth.

The movement of the ITCZ is responsible for the monsoon rains that fall in parts of the world. As we shall see later, monsoon conditions occur when winds blowing in one direction for part of the year change around and blow in the opposite direction for a period. These fluctuations can bring very dry weather alternating with very wet weather.

Beyond the sub-tropical zones outlined earlier, are areas dominated both in the northern and southern hemispheres by westerly winds. These occur at around latitudes 40° to 65° and are winds moving towards the poles bent westwards by the Coriolis effect. The temperate zones (see later) of the world fall within this area, including our own in western Europe. These areas are associated with very variable weather including winds which can be of ferocious strength. This is best exhibited by the westerlies of the southern hemisphere where the winds can howl over vast tracts of ocean largely unimpeded by land masses. Thus sailors termed the winds below 40°S the *Roaring Forties* because of their strength.

After the westerlies zone, the Hadley cell effect also occurs, though to a lesser extent than in the equatorial regions, at the poles. Some descending warm air does reach the poles from the tropics, and then winds emanate from the poles, as bitterly cold polar winds.

I have described above something of the way in which the so-called weather machine works, with the sun 'driving' the engine by heating the Earth, and the resulting winds that circulate around it. Another type of wind, which I touch on briefly in the section on winds which comes later, is the *jet stream* sometimes known as the *circumpolar vortex*. This wind, which can have a profound effect on the weather, is found in both hemispheres. It blows westwards at altitudes of around 10 kilometres (6 miles), sometimes with speeds of up to 480km/h (300mph). In the northern hemisphere the jet stream is intimately connected with the formation of high and low-pressure areas which form such a feature of our constantly changing weather. Winds in the jet stream normally blow from the west – the whole region of strong winds can move bodily north or south depending on the season. At times it oscillates like waves with the winds blowing from the north or south. When this north-south oscillation becomes very pronounced and the winds become slower, this can cause what is called in meteorological terms *stagnation*, and can lead to the foundation of what are known as *blocking highs*. Depending on the time of year these blocking highs can produce very dry, hot weather or cold, clear weather with frosts. The hot arid summer of 1976 was the result of such a blocking high.

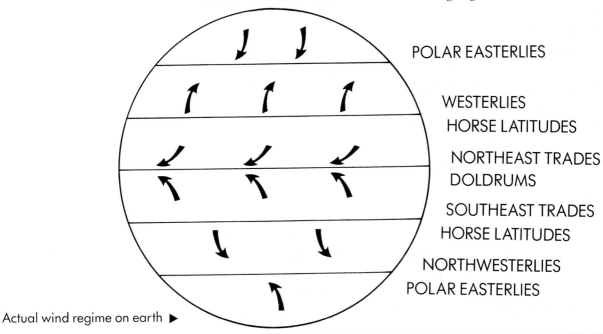

POLAR EASTERLIES

WESTERLIES
HORSE LATITUDES
NORTHEAST TRADES
DOLDRUMS
SOUTHEAST TRADES
HORSE LATITUDES
NORTHWESTERLIES
POLAR EASTERLIES

Actual wind regime on earth ▶

The pronounced movement of the jet stream in this way can also have a knock-on effect further south, for example the positioning of the ITCZ, with attendant consequences for rainfall in monsoon areas. This is just another example of how the weather of the world is interconnected, rather like a three-dimensional jigsaw puzzle.

The sun's heating of the Earth's atmosphere depends on three processes. One is *radiation*, that is the rays of the sun travelling through space and then striking and warming the Earth's surface. The next is *conduction*, when the warm surface of the Earth heats up a narrow band of atmosphere above it, in the way that a stove top heats the bottom of a saucepan. But the most important is *convection*, described above in looking at how the weather machine of the planet works – namely the process by which hot air expands and rises, setting off the global circulation of heat.

As well as the light rays that we see, the radiation that emanates from the sun contains infra-red waves which provide heat, X-rays, gamma-rays and ultraviolet rays which burn. However, the presence of ozone in the upper atmosphere (ozone is a form of oxygen with three atoms, O_3, compared to the normal O_2) filters out these more harmful rays. The present fears that have arisen over the ozone layer are based on the principle that any thinning of this may allow more of these harmful rays to reach the Earth.

Lightwaves themselves are affected by the Earth's atmosphere as they enter the planet. Light is made up of different colours – the 'colours of the rainbow'. As the blue spectrum of the light enters it is more easily scattered by the atmosphere than the others and it is this effect which causes the sky to appear blue. At evening, as the blue sky disappears, the red and orange end of the spectrum can be scattered if there is a haze in the sky, which causes spectacular sunsets.

The atmosphere of the Earth is central to its survival. As well as filtering out harmful rays from the sun, it contains the oxygen we breathe and also acts like a 'blanket', keeping in enough heat for the planet to survive and ensuring an equilibrium between energy coming in and energy going out of the planet. The part of the atmosphere in which we live is called the *troposphere* which is around 16 kilometres (10 miles) in height at the equator – about 5 kilometres (3 miles) less at the poles.

The upper limit of the troposphere is called the *tropopause.*

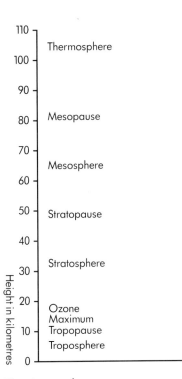

The Atmosphere.

Curiously this level is colder than the *stratosphere* above it, as the ozone particles in the latter absorb some of the sun's energy and act as a source of heat. This is important, for it means that the convection effect of warm air rising through the Earth's atmosphere stops at the tropopause (air rises if it is warmer than the air above it). This rising air stops at the tropopause which marks the boundary between the troposphere and stratosphere. The stratosphere extends some 50 kilometres (31 miles) up to the stratopause, the boundary with the next layer the mesosphere. Above this in the mesopause beautiful noctilucent clouds (see section on clouds) can be seen. In this stratum temperatures can be very low, down to -143°C (-225°F). Above this is the *thermosphere* which stretches from 88 kilometres (55 miles) to 496 kilometres (310 miles) and above that, and beyond the atmosphere itself, is the *exosphere* where satellites orbit.

Aside from the atmosphere there are other factors which can influence the heating of the Earth's surface by the sun. One is cloud cover. A thick layer of cloud, with its white shiny surfaces, can reflect back a good deal of the sun's heat. Another factor is dust in the atmosphere. This can arise from volcanic activity, such as the massive eruption of Krakatoa in 1883 when vast amounts of material were thrown up into the atmosphere where it lingered for many years. Similarly, and more recently, Mt St Helens erupted in 1980 churning out dust, though it is not widely thought to have had a huge impact on the weather because relatively little gas and dust was released. However, the presence of dust can block out the sun's rays to some extent and there is historical evidence that volcanoes in the past have had discernible climatic effects.

More controversial is the suggestion that dust from man's own activities like industry and mining may rise in sufficient quantities to affect the weather, though most experts doubt that this is likely. In any case, it is by no means clear whether such dust would reduce heating from the sun or have the reverse effect. For it could be that such dust could act rather like the lid of a cooking pot and reflect heat back down to the Earth's surface. Another area of study which is perceived as increasingly significant in looking at the planet's weather as a whole, is the relationship between the weather and the Earth's magnetic field.

The oceans play an essential role in the working of the weather machine. More than two-thirds of the planet's surface is covered by water, and since water is a better storehouse of energy from the sun than the land, the oceans provide the main source of heat energy in starting off the convection process outlined earlier. Furthermore, oceanic currents move in similar ways and follow broadly similar paths to the winds of the world and similarly help distribute heat around the globe. A well-known example of this is the Gulf Stream which crosses the North Atlantic and brings higher temperatures to western Europe including the British Isles. More and more scientists are looking at the ways that the effects of the oceans combine with atmospheric and wind changes to influence our weather.

It was once thought that the sun's energy source was constant and unchanging. In the last decade experts have discovered that the sun's emission of energy can fluctuate and it is conceivable that this may have some bearing on the Earth's climate. There is also a by now well-established link between sunspots, denoting increased activity on the sun's surface, and our weather. It would appear that activity on the sun follows an eleven-year cycle which correlates with weather patterns here. The evidence shows that when the sun is less active than normal there are correspondingly lower temperatures on Earth.

In the above analysis I have tried to show how our planet's climate is influenced by a wide variety of factors which in ways, not yet all fully understood, are interconnected and lead to the patterns that we experience. Understanding our climate cannot be achieved by looking at the one section in isolation but only by gradually piecing together the various blocks of weather until we arrive at a complete picture. This is part of the daunting task but also the great challenge that faces meteorologists around the world.

Elsewhere in the book I go into detail on different climates of the world and how phenomena such as storms, rain, low-pressure areas and clouds and fog are formed. But at this stage it is useful to put our present climatic concerns into context by looking backwards to see how weather has affected our planet since the dawning of time.

Weather: A Backwards Look

Nostalgia, they say, 'ain't what it used to be'. Neither, it seems is the weather. Historical evidence shows that the climate of the world since the planet was formed more than 4,000 million years ago has fluctuated greatly, and on many occasions has borne little resemblance to what we experience today.

For example, we are currently in the middle of an ice epoch (longer than an ice age) which has lasted millions of years and is likely to continue for millions more. Yet, in the context of the history of the planet, this is not a normal period. More average conditions would be significantly warmer, producing the lush vegetation and hot conditions that prevailed eons ago when dinosaurs walked the Earth for millions of years.

The reason why we are in the middle of such a cold epoch has a great deal to do with the positioning of the land masses. Almost imperceptibly, the great continents are constantly moving and changing location. Throughout the history of the Earth it has been unusual to have one polar ice-cap; it is unique for us now to have two of them. Normally the circulation of the warm currents of the oceans, as I mentioned earlier, helps distribute the heat and ensure a general uniformity of temperatures. However, the land mass that has become known to us as Antarctica has temporarily (in global terms!) positioned itself over the South Pole thereby blocking off warm currents. This has allowed ice some 1,800 metres (6,000 feet) thick to form a sheet over that now most inhospitable of continents.

Similarly, by another quirk of the slow drift of the continents, land has encircled the North Pole, causing the waters there to be largely cut off from the worldwide drift of oceanic currents. This too has allowed an ice-cap to develop at the North Pole. Eventually – and by this I mean in tens of millions of years – the land masses of North America and Europe, which are moving away from each other, will be far enough apart to allow the warmer currents from the Atlantic to warm up the Arctic and melt the ice-cap. However, as far as humans are concerned at present the existence of two polar ice-caps is, for all practical purposes, a permanent one.

We have already seen how the two ice-caps play their part in our weather system, with the transference, through a complex process, of warm air from the tropics making its way to the poles, where cold winds emerge influencing our weather. The polar ice-caps are also crucial in the formation of ice ages to which I shall now turn.

Ice Ages

Within an ice epoch there are *ice ages* which alternate with shorter warmer periods known as *interglacials*. At the moment the Earth is passing through an interglacial which has lasted for around 10,000 years following the last Ice Age, which in turn went on for some 100,000 years. It would appear from historical climatic evidence that this ice age/interglacial pattern was established at the beginning of this ice epoch. Perhaps ominously for man, the pattern suggests that ice ages last around 100,000 years on average and the shorter, warmer interglacials around 10,000 – so we are nearing the end of our current warmer period.

However, there is no need for any alarm at this thought. The next ice age could be up to 1,000 years or more away – a short period in climatology but a comfortingly lengthy one for us. And in any case no one can yet predict what effect the greenhouse effect (see later) may have on the overall pattern of global cooling and in arresting a return to glacial conditions.

What does seem apparent is that within the current interglacial, starting some 10,000 years ago, there have been smaller patterns emerging – periods of warmer weather, followed by colder weather and so on. These have been broken down by climatologists into four main periods. The first followed the end of the last Ice Age, indeed it caused it to end, and probably reached its warmest about 5,000 or 6,000 years ago. At

The Kiatgut Sermiat glacier in southern Greenland, showing patterns of crevasses.
Simon Fraser/Science Photo Library.

this time the temperature would have been on average about 2°C (3.6°F) warmer than the present day.

This period has acquired the name the Optimum period as a result, and was followed by a much colder spell which more or less coincides with the historical period call the Iron Age, which reached its coldest around 2,500 years ago. (It should be remembered that these changes are gradual and do not occur overnight.)

The next period, one less well known but much closer to our own time and therefore much better documented, was the so-called Little Optimum. This period of warming peaked in western Europe in around 1100 AD and coincided with a period of growth and agricultural and technological advance during what we call the Middle Ages. On average temperatures were around 1°C (1.8°F) lower than' now. Vineyards flourished in England and generally cultivation was possible on higher and more northerly ground than at present. Crops also grew on Greenland and at one point as the ice came down from the north, a polar bear was able to make it to the Faroe Islands!

However, the Little Optimum gave way by the late Middle Ages to a gradual cooling of the Earth that led to the Little Ice Age, which reached its peak 200 to 300 years ago. It was during this period that the Great Frost Fairs took place on the Thames as the river froze sufficiently to allow people – and even elephants! – to walk on it safely. (In the winter of 1683/4 a whole ox was roasted on the ice.) The water did freeze again in the 1890s but was not hard enough to support people. Again it should be remembered that even within this colder period there were some hot, dry spells, such as 1666, the year of the Great Fire of London.

Although it is widely accepted that the last Little Ice Age ended around 1850 there has been some speculation as to whether we are still in it and that our present warmer period could be but a brief respite. There is certainly evidence that the first half of this century was unusually warm compared with the last few hundred years and that, the greenhouse effect aside, we are heading for a cooler period. In any case, all historical climatic trends point to us nearing the end of our interglacial and gradually approaching the next age of ice.

What Causes the Ice Age?

Although as I said earlier our current ice epoch is essentially

Overleaf:
Plinian column of ash, gas and pulverised rock shooting out of Mt St Helens volcano, Washington State, USA during the second eruption of 22 July 1980.
Professor Stewart Lowther/Science Photo Library

Roman bridge over the Danube at the Iron Gates, undamaged by ice – AD 106-270.

caused by the positioning of the continents around the globe, this does not necessarily explain the subsequent pattern of long ice ages interspersed with much briefer periods of warming. The first important point is that ice ages should be seen on Earth as the norm rather than the exception. That is to say with the present continental arrangements balanced against the heat source from the sun, it is to be expected that ice ages will occur with huge glacial fields stretching across northern Europe, including the whole of the British Isles, and temperatures in the region on average some 10°C (18°F) lower than now.

It follows from this that it requires relatively unusual circumstances to produce the necessary warmth to force the glaciers back. The answer appears to lie in the orbital patterns of the Earth around the sun. I have already mentioned two orbital features of the Earth, one its elliptical orbit, the other the tilt of the Earth in relation to its plane of orbit. However, these eccentricities of orbit are not constant and fixed. The Earth's orbit changes from being almost a perfect circle to its elliptical form and then back again. This pattern can take around 100,000 years. Similarly, the Earth's tilt does not remain fixed at 66.5° to the plane but varies between 65.6° and 68.2° over a period of 40,000 years. At present the tilt is increasing.

There is a third quirk in the Earth's orbit, namely a 'wobble' in the Earth's axis of rotation caused by the pull of the moon and which has a cycle of approximately 24,000 years. The significance of these variations is that some sixty years ago a Yugoslavian geophysicist, Milankovitch, suggested that these alternations could account for the ice age/interglacial pattern. His argument was that only when these variations combined sufficiently to allow summers warm enough to melt the ice

sheets could the Ice Age be halted and temporarily forced back. Subsequent analysis of climatic history suggests that this indeed is what has happened in practice and that it is these orbital variations which account for our weather pattern during the present ice epoch.

This theory, known as the Milankovitch model, is now widely accepted as a good explanation of the ice-age cycle though it does not explain what may trigger an ice age, or cause the mini-cycles of optima and little ice ages. The reasons behind these may be a combination of complex factors including the Earth's magnetism, changes in the sun's heating and variations in the atmosphere caused both by natural forces like earthquakes or even, some say, by meteor strikes; and by man-made activities resulting in dust and fumes which could influence future climatic trends.

Climates of the World

The countries around the world do not fit into neat and precise categories of climate and weather. Nations, especially those as vast as the Soviet Union and the United States, may sprawl over several different climatic zones making life for one inhabitant very different from that of a fellow countryman living thousands of miles away. You only have to look at the contrast between life in California and life in New York to see this.

However, it is useful and valid to split regions of the world up and describe them according to the types of weather they experience and thus arrive at a number of describable weather patterns, or climates. I will begin with a look at the weather of our own country, which is part of a temperate climate, before moving on to the different and very varied climates of the world.

Temperate British Isles

It is a national pastime for many of us to talk about, and largely moan about, our weather; the weather is often the initial topic in any conversation.

There is a reason for this, in that our weather is changeable, influenced largely by the unsettling effect of low-pressure zones moving in with the prevailing westerly and south-westerly winds from the Atlantic. However, there are many reasons why instead of complaining about the weather – or blaming it on the forecaster! – we should be thankful for the climate that prevails on our shores.

Ours is part of a temperate climate, which is characterized by rainfall all year round, and a relatively small fluctuation in temperatures. The British Isles are in a maritime temperate zone, that is to say our weather is greatly influenced by the seas around us, which keep summer temperatures relatively cool but at the same time prevent very cold weather in winter. This is because unlike the land, the sea takes a comparatively long time to heat up and cool down. So after a summer of warm weather the seas around the British Isles retain warmth throughout much of the winter which helps to temper the impact of cold winds and cold air masses approaching us. On the other hand, when spring and early summer arrive the sea has cooled down and thus can be quite cold in May and June even though the weather may be warm and sunny – and any breezes coming off the sea will have a correspondingly cooling effect on the temperatures we feel.

Meteosat image of Europe,
Great Britain and Ireland.
*Photo Library International/Science Photo
Library.*

This is particularly true on the east coast of Great Britain with the waters of the cool, shallow North Sea. On a warm summer's day the air over the land is warmed, causing it to rise. To replace it the colder air over the sea moves in – the start of a sea breeze – which has the effect of reducing the temperature. However, this sea breeze is unlikely to extend right inland, so areas well away from the coast will be noticeably warmer than those on the coast.

Another, unseen, factor on our temperatures, especially in winter, is the Gulf Stream (or North Atlantic Drift) which brings warm waters across the ocean. These waters bathe our west coasts, keeping temperatures higher and reducing the chances of frost in winter for these coastal areas. It is significant that some of our coldest waters during winter are off the coast of Norfolk, which does not benefit from the effects of the Gulf Stream. Some of the warmest waters are off the coast of Cornwall where the sea might be a respectable 10°C (50°F) in winter, only 6°C (11°F) below the summer average.

All in all the seas around us, as well as being a useful protection against would-be invaders, are a good natural defence against extremes of very cold weather. Despite this, and even in a small country like the British Isles, there can still be quite large variations in climate. For example, on average Cambridge has something like a dozen days a year when the temperature will reach 25°C (77°F), whereas Lerwick in the Shetland Isles can sometimes go a full twelve months without registering as high as 18°C (64°F).

Another vital factor affecting our climate is the wind. Most people know that our *prevailing* wind is a south-westerly wind, which means simply that looking at records over a long period the wind from the south-west will be the most common. Quite why this is so is part of a complex global system of weather patterns. Part of the reason has to do with two relatively permanent weather features: one is a high-pressure area around the Azores; the other is the presence of low-pressure areas in the Atlantic to the north.

As one would expect, air starts to travel from high to low pressure and so it is with winds from the Azores which travel to the low-pressure areas to the north-west of the British Isles. But because the Earth is spinning, the winds do not travel in a straight line but are 'bent' in our direction by the *Coriolis* spin, or effect. This gives us winds from the south-west and west. The weather associated with these winds is generally warm and moist, giving drizzle and low cloud, but as we shall see shortly wind direction alone is not a perfect indicator of the type of weather we experience.

A wind from the due north, from the Arctic, is not very common but as one would expect it can bring very cold weather. As this extremely cold air is heated by the relatively warm sea to the north of the British Isles, low-pressure areas can form. These are called *polar lows*. They can be about the same size as an average county and can bring severe snow storms in winter. More common are north-westerlies which often bring showery weather; the frequency and intensity of the showers depending on whether it is summer or winter, day or night.

Winds from the south are not a common feature of British weather, but when they do arrive they can herald very fine, warm weather. They may originate over North Africa and pass over France, so they remain fairly dry and are unlikely to bring much rain on their own. However, many people have heard of the definition of an Englishman's summer as 'three fine days and a thunderstorm'. The truth behind this saying can be seen when a southerly wind bringing warm, dry weather to this country is met by a moist wind from the south-west. The mixture of warm air and moisture creates thunderstorms at altitude – maybe 3,000 metres (10,000 feet) – bringing thunder and sheet lightning and heavy downpours from France, often at night.

Easterly winds can bring very cold spells of weather, in fact it is winds from the east that produce our coldest weather.

The reason for this is that the easterly wind comes from the direction of the Soviet Union, a huge land mass which cools down in winter – it lacks the tempering influence of the sea – to extremely low temperatures. Easterly winds bring us this extreme cold and, unlike a northerly wind, the easterly wind only has a short distance to travel over the warming sea. It was easterly winds which brought the severe cold of the winters of 1947 and 1962/3 – two of the coldest winters this century in the British Isles.

Although the easterly wind is a dry wind, having blown mostly over land, it can pick up a little moisture over the North Sea and bring bands of low cloud over the east coast. In summer, the intense heating in the interior of Europe produces hot, thermal currents so beloved of glider pilots. This may be responsible for the fact that around twenty years ago many of the top gliders were Czechs or Poles, who lived in the path of these dry and warm easterly currents.

As I mentioned earlier, wind directions are a good indication

Ponsticill reservoir, Wales, in the summer drought of 1976.
Water Bulletin

of the type of weather that may be approaching, but they do not tell the whole story. If we consider that wind is moving air, then that air must have originated somewhere. A band of air which has an identifiable uniformity of temperature and humidity is what is known as an *air mass* and, while these often conform to the north, south, east and west wind patterns outlined above, complications can occur when the air masses become mixed up, or approach from an unexpected direction.

The most common air mass affecting the British Isles is the *polar maritime* which originates in the Arctic and reaches us after sweeping across the North Atlantic. The sea has the effect of warming it from below, producing clouds and showers in the unstable mass of air. In winter, this air mass will bring the worst weather to the north and west of the country, because as the air reaches inland there is insufficient warmth in the wintry sun to warm the ground below and continue the formation of showers. However, in summer this air mass can produce showers all over the country as the sun-lit ground heats up the air, causing it to rise and form showers over many areas.

A variation on this air mass, a *returning polar maritime*, also originates in the Arctic, but sweeps out wide into the Atlantic before making a homeward journey towards the pole. The difference here is that after initial warming in the middle of the Atlantic, the unstable elements are cooled in their lowest layers as the air mass begins to track northwards again. So, when it reaches the British Isles it tends to produce dull, overcast weather often with drizzle. However, enough instability survives in its upper reaches to be able to produce showers and even thunderstorms.

These two air masses, together with the *tropical maritime*, are the bands of air which most affect our weather. The tropical maritime comes from the Azores and further west in the Gulf of Mexico, so it is a warm, humid air mass. This mass keeps temperatures high in winter, often with damp, wet and overcast conditions with no chance of frost. In summer, the coastal regions of the West Country may still be hit by moist, damp weather especially on high ground.

The weather brought by a tropical maritime air mass will be mild and humid rather than hot, except for parts of the east or south-east of the country. Generally speaking, areas which are to the east and in the lee of high ground experience the best weather when such an air mass prevails. A good example is east

Violent winter storm battering Porthleven, Cornwall, on the morning of 17 December 1989.
David Brenchley/Cornish Photonews

Devon which lies in the lee of Dartmoor. Tropical maritime weather is often 'muggy' and oppressive. It produces fog on coasts and hills and, while it wards off low temperatures, it does not always feel pleasant.

Less common is the *Arctic* air mass, blowing directly from the pole and which, as mentioned above in the context of northerly winds, can produce heavy snow showers. It was an Arctic air mass which produced a severe spell of snow during late March and early April 1975 – the snow was dry and powdery, indicating it came from a very cold air mass.

The air mass bringing the coldest temperatures is the *polar continental* mass which comes in from the Soviet Union. Fortunately, it is not that common. The polar continental is usually a dry air mass, having little distance to travel over the sea. On occasions it can cross over the North Sea from Scandinavia, which gives it a chance to pick up moisture that falls as snow on the east coast in winter.

Last and least common over the British Isles is the *tropical continental* air from the south, originating from North Africa. This brings warm, dry weather. Sometimes it carries red Saharan dust which falls with rain, leaving a reddish film over buildings and parked vehicles in southern England. (Before leaving air masses let me mention that you can read about what happens when different ones meet out in the Atlantic on page 118 – the result can be low-pressure zones tracking towards the British Isles.)

Snow plough clearing a country lane following a snow storm.
Dr Jeremy Burgess/Science Photo Library.

The difference between the weather we experience in the summer and that in the winter is due, in part, to the tilt in the Earth's axis producing shorter days and less sunlight in winter. However, another significant factor is the development of highs and lows out in the Atlantic. We have seen how the semi-permanent high around the Azores – one of several at that latitude in the northern and southern hemispheres – can help direct winds towards our shores. During the winter months this high tends to recede slightly, so that the lows which form in the Atlantic, instead of passing between Scotland and Iceland, are dragged further south towards the British Isles, bringing with them unsettled, wet and windy weather.

So far I have been discussing mainly *advective* weather development, that is weather which has essentially developed elsewhere and then reached the British Isles. But weather can, and does, develop on a more local level. Sea breezes and localized showers or thunderstorms on a summer's day are regular examples. And of course, the weather that any given spot in the British Isles experiences will depend on local factors

Frost fair on the River Thames
1683-84.
Hulton Picture Company

of altitude, shelter given by trees or mountains, soil type, and whether we are discussing the open countryside, or built-up areas where temperatures are generally higher.

Other Temperate Regions

The hallmark of temperate zones is a relatively small fluctuation in temperature between the seasons with rain that generally falls all year round. Temperate areas of the world other than Britain include much of the rest of Europe, parts of the north-west and north-east of the United States, New Zealand, eastern Asia and southern Chile. However, some of these areas experience quite different types of weather depending on their position relative to the sea and winds. For example, although the north-east of North America is at the same latitude as western and northern Europe, it lacks the warming influence of the North Atlantic Drift. As a consequence, much of the north-eastern seaboard of the United States is ice-bound during winter months.

For different reasons, parts of temperate eastern Asia also experience quite cold winters. This is as a result of the winds blowing out from the interior of Eurasia during the winter when the land mass is extremely cold.

Again, temperate zones which are further inland will tend to get a considerable amount of their rainfall during the summer from *convection*, that is when the sun heats the ground sufficiently to cause moist air to rise, forming clouds and then rain. Temperate zones, such as Europe, get more of their rain in the winter from the effect of low-pressure zones coming in from the Atlantic driven by the prevailing westerlies. Hilly areas can get extra rainfall from what is known as the *orographic* effect which occurs where air is forced to rise over high ground, causing clouds followed by rain. Scotland and Wales, Norway and the South Island of New Zealand are areas subject to this type of rainfall. This can occur at any time of year though it is more common in late summer when the warmer seas provide greater moisture in the air.

Although temperate zones account for only about seven per cent of the world's land surface, they are by far the most popular areas in which to live and are home to around four-tenths of the Earth's population. This is largely due to the mildness of the climate, which prevents conditions from becoming too harsh, a plentiful supply of rain and generally very fertile soils.

With the exception of parts of New Zealand where the land is inaccessible, most of the temperate zones' natural and very rich forest vegetation has been cleared to make way for more intensive farming methods, of the type we are familiar with in the British Isles. Deciduous trees, such as the oak and the beech, are the most commom type of tree found in the temperate zones. These have formed a protective mechanism against the effects of cold winters by shedding their leaves. Many people regret that the more featureless but hardier coniferous trees have become more widespread in this country – though measures are now being taken to plant an increasing number of native deciduous trees.

Gathering grapes probably in an English medieval vineyard, as depicted in the calendar section of the Peterborough Psalter, mid 13th century.
Professor H. H. Lamb

Mediterranean

Over the last twenty years the Mediterranean has become the main destination for Europeans, especially the British, seeking sunny summer holidays. Looking at the climate of the coastal fringes of the sea it is not hard to see why – long hot summers, with more or less guaranteed sunshine, and mild, wetter winters. In fact this mildness has encouraged not just tourists but people retiring there permanently, away from the cool and occasionally cold winters of Britain.

The Mediterranean climate is a form of temperate climate and is used to refer not just to the area around the Mediterranean Sea (including North Africa) but to similar climates around the world such as those in California, parts of Chile, south-west Australia and South Africa. All are characterized by hot summers and an abundance of sunshine all year. In winter, temperatures rarely drop below 5°C (41°F) and are more likely to be in the region of 12° to 13°C (53° to 55°F) while in summer averages can be up to 27°C (80°F).

Frosts are very rare in a Mediterranean climate although when they do occur they can cause great damage to crops. For this reason, vulnerable crops such as citrus fruits are usually planted on sloping terrain rather than in valley floors, where in a cold spell frosts are likely to occur as cold air collects in the valley bottom.

Mediterranean regions are widely settled and well cultivated but unpleasant winds can sometimes cause problems to man and crops alike. In California the Santa Ana wind, a hot and arid wind from inland desert regions, causes disagreeably dry living conditions, as well as damaging plants and increasing the risk of fires in tinder-dry vegetation. The Mediterranean itself suffers from the famous, or infamous, mistral, a cold and dry wind that blows up the Rhône valley in France causing widespread crop damage. Farmers have planted cypress-tree hedges to protect crops from its worst effects. Another dry Mediterranean wind, this time a hot one, is the scirocco from North Africa which frequently carries large amounts of dust from the desert.

Many plants have adapted themselves to the demands of a Mediterranean climate, none more so than the olive tree which is a distinctive feature of the landscape. Its tough leaves and thick bark help it cope with the excessive heat and dryness of the summer months. It is also in Mediterranean climates that much of the world's Citrus is grown.

Continental or Steppeland

This is a type of climate which occurs mainly in the interior of great land masses, hence the description 'continental'. The word *steppe* is a Russian one, meaning open grassy plains without forest; it has come to be used for all such similar areas around the world.

Steppe climate falls broadly into two categories: one in the northern hemisphere and one in the southern hemisphere. The northern steppe areas lie in the central Soviet Union and constitute the prairie lands of North America. Both areas are far away from the moderating influence of the sea and this gives them warm, but short, summers, and long, cold winters, sometimes made worse by blizzards sweeping across the wide open plains.

Those steppe areas found in the southern hemisphere are parts of South Africa (the veld), parts of Argentina (the pampas) and parts of Australia, where the climate is made more moderate by the relative proximity to the equator and the influence of the seas. Such temperate grasslands – another term for this form of climatic region – have warmer winters.

In East Africa, the temperate grasslands are home to much of the world's larger wildlife such as lions, giraffe, wildebeest and hyenas. In summer, when the rains come, the plains are filled with vegetation many feet high and are an impressive sight. Similar lands in North America and the Soviet Union were once occupied by hunters tracking after the abundant prey such as the herds of bison which characterized the region.

Now, particularly in the United States and the Soviet Union, temperate grasslands have been widely turned over to large-scale agriculture and, because of their fertile soil, they have become known as the 'granaries' of the world, producing vast amounts of grain. Unfortunately in the Soviet Union, westerly winds bringing the necessary moisture to sustain such crops have become less common, occasionally causing the grain-bearing crops to fail. The prairies have also suffered in the past from shortages of rain, notably in the 1930s when the presence of the Rocky Mountains removed moisture from the air, causing the land to become drier and dustier. Eventually the appalling

Drought damaged crops at Gilbertville, Iowa in June 1988.
Associated Press

'dust bowl' conditions developed, made famous in John Steinbeck's novel *The Grapes of Wrath*.

It was once thought that these grasslands were too dry to be able to support trees, but subsequent research has shown that trees could survive on the plains which may have once been forested. However, the presence of man and livestock means the forests are unlikely ever to return.

Tropical

Tropical climates are probably the most exotic of all in the world, associated as they are with thick, luscious jungle or rain forest, and a rich variety of plants, insects and animals. To someone used to the changeability of the British weather, however, the weather routine in the tropics may, at first sight, seem a little monotonous. Rain, often very heavy downpours, is likely to occur every day more or less at the same time. The days begin sunny and hot, and with the tropics situated within a ten-degree band either side of the equator the sun is directly overhead. As the day wears on the heat causes the extremely humid air to rise. Clouds form quickly often resulting in showers in the late afternoon, which usually clear to give a fine evening.

Temperatures in the tropics remain constantly high throughout the year, with as little as 2°C (3.6°F) separating the highest noon temperature from the lowest throughout the year. There are no real seasons, indeed it is said that night-time is the winter of the tropics. However, nights are also very warm and sticky, and unless there are cooling sea breezes life in the tropics can feel very humid and unpleasant to those not used to it.

The best-known tropical areas are the Amazon rain forest in South America which is fed by the huge Amazon river, the Congo basin in Central Africa, Malaysia, Indonesia and southern Vietnam. Typical of such jungle areas are massively tall trees whose leaves meet at the top to form a kind of canopy. Beneath, in the semi-twilight, grow smaller trees and ferns, but there is little undergrowth itself as sunlight finds it hard to penetrate the dense foliage.

There is, however, all sorts of abundant wildlife and a large number of plants which have yet to be properly studied and classified. Animals like monkeys, jaguars and multicoloured birds are residents of these jungles though many are becoming increasingly rare as man develops more and more of the rain forests of the world.

In fact the destruction of the rain forests is now being seen as a major environmental problem for the planet. Some estimates claim that destruction of the rain forests at the present rate would mean that by the end of the 20th century there will be little left. The impact is not just on the dwindling numbers of indigenous people who still inhabit the rain forests, or the flora and fauna. Rain forests are known to contain around 40 per cent of all carbon existing in plant life on Earth. The cutting and burning of those forests – the standard technique to clear them – may well have a major impact on the greenhouse effect, as well as on local water cycles; it is predicted that clearance of all the Amazon rain forest would reduce local rainfall by 20 per cent. Environmentalists are now calling for controls on the removal of the rain forests as research goes on into its likely impact.

Polar

The polar regions represent the harshest climate known to man, especially that of the Antarctic which surrounds the South Pole. The coldest temperature ever recorded in nature was at Vostock in the Antarctic where an incredible -88°C (-126°F) was measured at a Soviet research station.

The Antarctic is a land mass, a continent in its own right, but one which is buried in ice sometimes miles deep. As if this was not enough, the bleak terrain of the South Pole is frequently ravaged by hurricane-force winds causing blizzards and bringing further misery to any life form unfortunate enough to be there. The crew of one ship, the *Belgica*, had the dubious pleasure of being the first people to winter in the Antarctic when the ship became stuck fast in the ice in February 1898. It was nearly another year before the exploration ship broke free from the ice, by which time the horrific conditions, the darkness and the cold, had had a terrible effect on the crew.

The harshness of the environment was tragically emphasized in 1912 when Captain Scott and his companions perished in those lonely polar wastes.

Not surprisingly very little wildlife has chosen to make this bleak landscape its home. One animal that does survive there is the emperor penguin, a hardy bird which breeds on sea ice off the coast of the continent. It manages to rear its young by incubating a single egg between its feet and somehow the chick inside can withstand temperatures as low as -50°C (-58°F). Apart from scientists in lonely research stations no humans live there.

Icebergs in Biscoe Islands,
Antarctic Peninsula.
Simon Fraser/Science Photo Library

The Arctic, surrounding the North Pole, is by comparison slightly warmer, though still bitterly cold by any other standard. Unlike the Antarctic, the North Pole has no land mass of its own and lies in a sea of permanent ice with Greenland and North America as its nearest land masses. In common with the South Pole it experiences long, dark winters with no sun and long summers when it is transformed into the 'Land of the Midnight Sun' and the sun never sets. In the Arctic the summer brings a brief flourishing of small shrubs and plants and in comparison to the Antarctic, wildlife is plentiful. Caribou take advantage of the supplies of vegetation in the brief spring and summer. Animals such as polar bears and the beautiful arctic fox also seem to thrive in the conditions, while migrating birds pay visits in summer to feed on the plant life.

The traditional inhabitants of the Arctic region are the Eskimos or Inuit who have survived ingeniously by adapting to the rigours of their harsh environment. With the advent of modern technology and clothing life has become somewhat more tolerable.

Sand dunes, USA.

Desert

As one would imagine deserts experience some of the world's highest temperatures but perhaps more surprisingly they also undergo some of the greatest temperature contrasts to be found on the planet.

The sun beating down through clear desert skies causes the temperatures to soar. But when night falls there is no cloud cover to prevent the heat radiating from the ground escaping, and no moisture in the air which in other climates acts as an insulator. So the desert traveller may experience appalling heat during the day and a cold, even frosty, night.

Deserts occur when the annual rainfall is less than about 25 centimetres (10 inches), though some deserts are colder and drier than others. The most famous desert in the world is the Sahara, covering much of North Africa, and where one of the highest-ever shade temperatures was recorded – 58°C (136°F). But there are many other deserts too like the Simpson and Great Sandy in Australia, the Gobi in central Asia, the Kalahari in south-west Africa and the Sonora desert in Mexico, to name just a few.

Deserts are not simply a result of harsh climatic conditions, though this is certainly a large factor. The impact of man plays a part too – by removing trees and protective vegetation, and introducing livestock which destroy much of the plant life that once existed. There is also some evidence that deserts are extending, which could have ominous effects on human populations nearby.

As in the Arctic, though for very different reasons, life is a grim struggle for desert inhabitants. Many, such as the Australian Aborigines and the Tuareg of North Africa have survived as nomads, wandering after food and water as best they can. Occasionally oases exist such as the remarkable oasis at the Gorges du Todra in Morocco where the greenness caused by a high water table in the ground is in stark contrast to the aridity around it.

Only the hardiest of plants can survive the deserts; one of these is the cactus, now a familiar house plant in this country.

It has a very tough outer skin to resist the heat and is able to store large amounts of water on the rare occasions when rain falls. Other plants lie dormant as seeds for long periods, months or even years, waiting for a downpour.

When rain does eventually fall they mature and bloom very

quickly and shed more seeds which, in turn, will lie in wait for the next rains. This sudden flowering brings about remarkable 'desert bloom' when a normally barren landscape is brightened briefly by many colourful plants. (West Australian deserts are famous for this.)

Insects and snakes also cope well with these conditions. Take the sidewinder snake, for example, which has developed its distinctive sidewinding movement to ensure that not all of its body is touching the burning sand at any one time. Another hardy desert beast is the camel which can store great amounts of water to sustain it for long periods. The camel also has the capacity to foam at the mouth when it overheats. This foam spreads over part of the animal's body and then evaporates in the sun, so reducing its temperature.

Monsoon

Monsoon zones exist all around the world, for example Chile, North America, Africa and Australia, and not just in India and south-east Asia where we are most familiar with them. The main characteristic is that there are two seasons, wet and dry, caused by winds which blow in opposite directions. South-east Asia experiences north-east monsoons in winter and south-east monsoons in summer.

In the dry season, a stable mass of air rests over a monsoon region, and dry winds come from the interior of the land bringing fine weather. In the wet season, when temperatures rise over the land, the air there becomes warmer than that over the sea. As this warm air rises, cooler air from the sea moves in to replace it bringing with it the very moist air that causes the exceptionally high rainfall associated with monsoons. In the northern hemisphere, the rainy season usually starts around May and works on through the summer with heavy rain in June, July and August. In the monsoon zones of the southern hemisphere, like that of north and north-eastern Australia, the wettest months are January and February.

Monsoons vary according to the part of the world in which they occur, with the monsoon in the eastern Soviet Union accompanied by cold, freezing weather in winter.

In some monsoon regions, such as those in China, Japan and eastern Australia there can be rainfall all year round, although most of it will still fall in the wet, summer season.

However, in the more 'classic' monsoons of India up to three-quarters of the annual rainfall may fall in just three summer months. The agricultural culture of countries like this is based on the expected arrival of the monsoon rains to water crops. Unfortunately, as we have seen from the news in recent years, the monsoons can also bring with them appalling flooding and loss of life. On the other hand, there have been times when the monsoon rains have 'failed', bringing about a tragic chain reaction of ruined harvests and widespread famine.

Taiga

The climate of the Taiga, named after a Russian word, is a phenomenon of the northern hemisphere. The Taiga stretches below the Arctic regions of the Soviet Union and North America, and is characterized by short, warm summers and very long and very cold, severe winters. The main physical feature of the Taiga is the forests of coniferous trees which range for hundreds of miles. The coniferous tree is best adapted to such an unpromising climate, with branches that shed snow easily and needle-like leaves which provide little resistance to the howling winds that blow across these desolate regions.

The Siberian Taiga has recorded the lowest temperatures outside the Antarctic, a very chilly -68°C (-90°F) at Verkhoyansk. Exceptionally cold winds are largely responsible, bringing bitterly cold air from the Arctic Circle: the lack of cloud cover on clear winter nights only serves to let temperatures fall even lower still.

Worldwide Extremes of Temperature and Rainfall

Highest Temps
Azizia, Libya 58C
Vanda Station, Antarctica 15C
Cloncurry, Queensland 53C
Tirat Tsvi, Israel 54C
Death Valley, Arizona 57C
Seville, Spain 50C

Lowest Temps
Ilfrane, Morocco −24C
Vostok, Antarctica −89C
Charlotte Pass, Kosciusko Mts, NSW −22C
Oymekon, USSR −68C
Yukon, Canada −63C
Ust Shchugor, USSR −55C

Largest Annual Rainfall
Debundscha, Cameroon 10290mm
Tully, Queensland 4550mm
Mt. Waialeale, Hawaii 11680mm
Cherrapunji, Assam 11430mm
Vancouver Is., Canada 6500mm
Crkvice, Yugoslavia 4650mm

Lowest Annual Rainfall
Wadi Halfa, Sudan Less than 2.5mm
Mulka, South Australia 102.9mm
Aden, Yemen 45.7mm
Bataques, Mexico 30.5mm
Astrakan, USSR 162.5mm

Despite these factors, temperatures can sometimes reach quite high values in the summer – Verkhoyansk once recorded around 36°C (97°F) – which gives the region a massive contrast in temperature extremes.

These cold, forest regions still contain some of the world's larger wildlife, such as bears, lynx and moose, although as civilization pushes ever outwards into these inhospitable lands their numbers diminish. For man the Taiga regions are still most useful as a source of softwoods to make paper.

Weather Phenomena

The phenomena which make up the weather are all around us. Rain, clouds, snow, sun, fog and winds – all of these are part of our everyday lives which we often take for granted. Only occasionally, during a very bad storm or in exceptionally high winds, does the average person stop to think what may cause these essential components of life on Earth. In this section I want to look at these individual elements and explain how they form, giving at the same time some examples of their impact and force. For no matter how benign we think our climate, the weather is part of nature – and can strike a devastating blow when we least expect it.

Clouds

Clouds tend to be the poor relation of our weather, often overlooked by the man in the street in favour of the more obvious manifestations of weather such as rain, wind or snow. This is despite the fact that in this country, even in summer, scarcely a day goes by without a cloud passing somewhere overhead.

In fact clouds are of crucial importance in understanding the weather and have been the subject of detailed study by meteorologists for many years. After all, it is the clouds that bring – or fail to bring – the rain that waters our crops and the snow which covers much of northern Europe each winter. They also form those spectacular thunder and lightning storms which either delight or terrify us. By themselves, clouds are responsible for those gloomy autumn days which have such an impact on our moods – especially in Scandinavia where the suicide rate is said to rise during this dull, overcast weather, as people wait for the first snowfalls to arrive. Not least, clouds can provide some of the most beautiful sights imaginable, especially early in the morning or at dusk when the sun's reddish glow can adorn the sky with wonderful patterns and shades of colour.

Elsewhere in the book, in the chapter on reading weather charts, it is necessary to go into detail on how clouds are formed but it may be useful to give a brief explanation here.

Air contains water in the form of vapour, and the amount it can contain depends on factors such as pressure and temperature – warm air can hold more water vapour than cold air. When the air becomes saturated with water vapour it reaches what is known as the *dew point*, at which it condenses into clouds. This is assisted by the presence in the air of tiny particles around which droplets condense, called condensation nuclei.

These conditions occur in nature when you get warm, moist air rising into the atmosphere where as it gets higher it cools. As the colder air cannot hold so much water vapour, this water starts to condense, forming the clouds we see around us.

Essentially, there are two basic forms of cloud. *Layer* cloud is formed, as its name might suggest, when a large mass of air rises, forming sheets or layers of cloud. These clouds – which use the general name stratus – tend to be associated with stable weather and can produce those uniformly leaden skies and persistent rain with which we are so familiar in this country.

The other main type, *heap* clouds, do not tend to cover the sky completely, like layer clouds, but rise upwards and develop vertically – sometimes to great heights. These are formed when pockets of warm air rise very quickly, causing the clouds to form quickly.

This type of cloud is associated with hot summery days, with the approach of a cold front, or when cold air is heated quickly from below creating fast updraughts or forming rain. The large *cumulus* is an example of this kind of cloud, the sort associated with a shower on a summer's day. If there is sufficient energy in the updraught and sufficient moisture, such conditions can produce violent thunderstorms, which I will deal with later.

Classes of Cloud

Although, as I said earlier, it is possible to discern two basic forms of cloud, because of the huge variety that occur in nature, they are officially classified by the World Meteorological Organization into ten types. Within these ten classes there can be subspecies, forms of cloud which can occur in one or more of the basic types. For example the *castellanus* form, which has a castle-like look to it, can develop in a *cirrus* or *cirrocumulus* cloud.

Cirrus – These are high-altitude clouds, found at around 6,000 metres (20,000 feet) but can be at a much lower height in the cold polar regions. Their height means that cirrus clouds are made up of ice crystals and have a feathery, wispy appearance.

Cirrus cloud.
David Parker/Science Photo Library.

Cirrostratus – These are also high-altitude clouds. As the second part of the name suggests, the cirrostratus is a layer cloud and covers much of the sky. It can often be the herald of bad weather and produce a halo effect around the sun or moon, which people have used for centuries as a sign of rain.

Cirrostratus with altostratus.
Kim Westerkov/Oxford Scientific Films.

Cirrocumulus clouds.
David Parker/Science Photo Library.

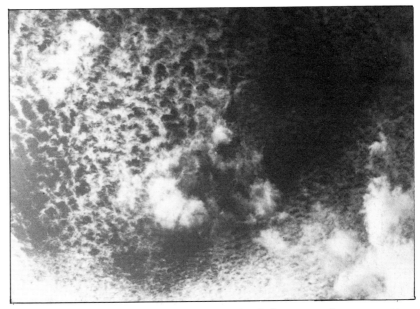

Cirrocumulus – High ice clouds which form regular, attractive patterns. They are a heaped form of cirrus.

These three are all high clouds – the next section in the ten types are the medium-altitude clouds, that is those at around 2,000-5,000 metres (6,500-16,500 feet).

Altocumulus – Often seen as flattened globules of cloud, they are mixtures of ice and super-cooled water and appear white and grey. They are sometimes the first sign of one of those thunderstorms that mark the end of a long hot spell.

Altocumulus clouds.
Doug Allan/Science Photo Library.

Altostratus clouds.
C. S. Broomfield.

Altostratus – Layer clouds which often signal impending rain. They are dull grey which usually makes the sun look very milky.

Nimbostratus – These are a thicker, lower version of the altostratus, and are always associated with rain or snow, and can make even daytime go very dark.

The final four of the ten are all low clouds, that is with bases at below 2,000 metres (6,500 feet).

Stratocumulus – These water clouds are grey or white but have darker areas within them. Often rounded or rolled in appearance. Probably the most common cloud.

Stratocumulus clouds.
Simon Fraser/Science Photo Library.

Nimbostratus clouds.
Breck P. Kent/Oxford Scientific Films.

Stratus – These are grey water clouds forming a uniform layer and often producing either drizzle or snow. The lowest cloud in the sky – called fog if it covers hills or coasts.

Cumulus clouds.
P. J. B. Nye.

▼ Stratus clouds.
S. D. Burt.

Cumulus – The best way to describe their appearance is cauliflower-like. They are heaped clouds, grey at the base but brilliant white on the top, and have a well-defined form. Arguably the most photogenic cloud.

Cumulonimbus – Last but by no means least, these are very striking clouds which can develop to heights of 12,000 metres (40,000 feet) with tremendous power and energy. They are colloquially known as thunderclouds and often have a distinctive anvil-like head. As they reach the upper atmosphere the top becomes icy and fibrous in appearance. It is these clouds that can produce tremendous storms.

Cumulonimbus clouds.
Robin Scagell/Science Photo Library.

Although clouds are classified into types they can and do take on many different forms. In Shakespeare's *Hamlet*, the young Prince Hamlet has fun at the expense of the king's advisor, Polonius, over the shape of a cloud he sees through a window, variously describing it in the shape of a camel, weasel and a whale. The grovelling Polonius agrees with each. Some of the most spectacular formations occur around mountain tops. As air approaches a mountain it is forced to rise to go over it, causing cloud to form and meaning that many peaks, such as in the Lake District and the Himalayas, are almost permanently shrouded. Clouds of this type take on a hump-backed, or lens-like shape which gives them the name *lenticular*.

In South Africa the Table Mountain near Cape Town is often covered by a delicate cloud, bringing it the name of the Tablecloth.

Lenticular clouds.
Henry Lansford/Science Photo Library.

Some of the most striking clouds are those known as *mountain wave* clouds. These occur on the lee side of a mountain, when the wind has blown up over a mountain top, falls down the other side, but then continues to oscillate up and down like a wave. Each time the air moves up into the condensation point a cloud is formed, which disperses as the air moves down again. Thus a neat little pattern of clouds gradually appears in the lee of the mountain which, despite the wind, appears stationary.

I recall how young trainee forecasters were given the task to measure wind speeds at altitude with a theodolite and were told by the old hands among us to observe these mountain wave clouds which they had never seen before. They were often amazed to find they had recorded the wind speed as nil – even though they knew there was wind!

A related form of cloud is the beautiful *nacreous* or *mother-of-pearl* cloud. These wonderful high-altitude forms are at heights of up to 32 kilometres (20 miles) and are seen at dawn or dusk when the sun, which is below the horizon, lights them up in a stunning way. It is thought they are also created by mountain wave effects but move high up into the stratosphere. Higher still are the brilliant *noctilucent* clouds which can be as high as 80 kilometres (50 miles) and can move at up to 480km/h (300mph).

Another high-flying phenomenon is the path left by a jet aircraft, now such a frequent part of our skies. These streams, which can be very attractive in certain lights, are known as *contrails* and are caused by the hot water vapour and gases which leave the aircraft and condense quickly in the cold air. Where an aircraft passes through a cloud and leaves a clear stream behind it, this is called *distrail*.

Fog

Many people wonder how fog differs from cloud. The answer is that, essentially, it does not and it is really part of the same phenomenon. Like cloud, fog forms when the moisture in the air is cooled until it reaches its dew point. At this stage the air is unable to retain all the moisture in the form of water vapour and condenses. The main difference between cloud and fog is that whereas cloud forms when the air rises, and cools, most of the fog occurs when air is cooled near the ground.

By far the most common form is known as *radiation fog*, so-called after the way it is formed. The ground, which is a good conductor of heat, takes in heat during the day from the sun, but at night radiates this heat out, cooling itself and the air in contact with it in the process. If it cools sufficiently, some water vapour will condense into cloud droplets on the ground, forming what we call fog.

It is a fallacy that fog develops most on very still nights. In fact if the weather is perfectly calm only a very thin layer of fog will appear or even just a dew. What is needed is a slight wind, of around 8km/h (5mph), to 'stir up' the cold air and create condensation in a wider area, thereby causing a thicker layer of fog. If the wind is too great the condensation may lift the fog off the ground and form low cloud. These factors make fog quite hard to forecast.

As is easily observed, fog occurs often in small valleys and hollows. This is because the air at the side of the valleys cooled by the night, 'pours' down the sides of the valley like a liquid, cooling the bottom where the condensation then forms.

It follows from what I have said so far that this radiation fog does not occur over large lakes or seas because these large bodies of water are generally warm enough to prevent the necessary cooling of the air. However, as any person living on the east coast of Great Britain knows, sea fogs can and do occur, sometimes forming a major menace for shipping.

Sea fogs are formed when a warm stream of air passes over cold water, cooling the lower layer of air below its dew point. A good example of this is the *haar* which affects coastal districts of eastern Scotland and parts of eastern England. Haars are most common in late spring and early summer when the sea is still relatively cold after the winter and the wind is blowing from the east, where continental Europe has begun to warm up. This fog can seem literally to be coming in on the tide.

A more exotic, and attractive, form of fog is what is often called *arctic sea smoke*. This is created in the opposite way to sea fog, that is, it occurs when cold air passes over (relatively) warm water. As its name suggests, this steam-like fog is found mostly in polar regions where winds from ice-covered land pass over water which is ice-free and therefore warmer.

Another point of confusion for some people is the difference between fog and *mist*. Again, these are part of the same process and differ essentially only when visibility is less than 200 metres (650 feet): that is a fog; otherwise it is a mist. A fog also has a relative humidity of not less than 95 per cent.

As we all know fog can be a killer, especially on roads where banks of fog appear interspersed by bright sunlight. Fog has also brought about the demise of many ships, which have run aground or into other vessels while the crew have been unaware of where they were going.

Another associated menace – made by man – is that of *smog*. This word, from the contraction of smoke and fog, gives us a clue as to its origins. As I have mentioned, condensation is assisted by the presence of small particles in the air. Air pollution makes fog – or smog – easier to form and means it hangs around much longer. Such smog can be a killer. The Victorian age saw what were called 'pea-soupers' affecting newly industrialized cities. As recently as 1952 London was hit by a severe December smog when, with an estimated 1,000 tons of dirt particles in the air, up to 4,000 people died in the London area, mostly from associated respiratory illnesses.

The condition that can cause smogs to develop and linger is what is known as the *inversion* of temperatures. Temperatures normally fall with increasing height above ground and this means that pollution can disperse upwards. Occasionally, though, the situation may be reversed by a mass of warm, descending air. This warm air, termed the *inversion layer*, sits above the cold and traps any pollution beneath it. This leads to a build-up of the pollutants and so smog forms.

A modern phenomenon, and one which has hit London, is the photochemical smog where sunlight acts on car exhaust fumes and releases irritant gases which can cause tiredness and coughing. Sunny Los Angeles is particularly badly affected by this!

Precipitation
1 Rain

It may come as some surprise to readers, but up to 95 per cent of all rain that falls in this country began its existence as snow. Most of the clouds that give rain are of sufficient altitude for them to contain ice crystals which, in turn, become snow flakes in the right conditions.

Although rain is so common (at least in this part of the world) the process which causes it to form is by no means simple and has been a constant source of scientific investigation. The most important theory is the *Bergeron-Findeison* effect, named after its Swedish and German proponents. This explains how, in a complex inter-reaction at temperatures between -10°C (14°F) and -20°C (-4°F), water vapour, super-cooled water droplets and ice crystals help produce larger crystals, which eventually fall out of the clouds as snow. In our climate the air is generally warm enough during descent to melt the flakes, forming rain.

However, this theory does not explain rain in tropical regions where the temperatures are not sufficient for the clouds to form too many ice crystals. On such occasions rain is explained by the *coalescence* of water droplets, that is the droplets colliding with each other until they reach sufficient size to fall to the Earth as rain. In thinner cloud the drops will collide with fewer other drops and the resulting smaller rain droplets are what is called drizzle.

What forecasters usually refer to as rain comes from the layer-type cloud mentioned in the section on clouds, whereas when we talk about showers we mean periods of rain between which there will be a brightening up of conditions. Incidentally, one should not suppose that drizzle means hardly any water is falling – in the right conditions a day's drizzle can produce quite a measurable amount of water.

Of course, rain is one of the essential life-giving elements of Earth, producing the water we drink and the water to irrigate crops. We are lucky that, in general, we have a balanced, temperate climate that allows a good mixture of rain and sun, even though there can be large variations in rainfall between one part of the British Isles and another. High areas of land, such as Dartmoor in Devon, act as a rain shadow and deprive the area in its lee of a great deal of rainfall. Thus south-east Devon is traditionally drier than north and west Devon. Sometimes exceptional weather can remind us just how fragile this balance is. The extended dry spell of 1975/6 and 1988/9 left many areas short of water and looking more like a Mediterranean country.

Equally, too much water can occur. In 1952 a flash flood destroyed much of Lynmouth in north Devon, killing more than thirty people. Much more recently, in January 1990, there was the worst flooding in some parts of the British Isles for forty years.

However, globally the contrast can be far more striking. The town of Calama, in the arid Atacama desert of north Chile, was said to have been without rain for 400 years, since around 1570 (the time when Queen Elizabeth I was on the throne). In 1972, not only did this drought end but much of the town was damaged or destroyed by appalling floods which cut electricity and caused landslides.

In 1972 more than 130 people were killed when a flash flood swept through Big Thompson Canyon in Colorado in the United States. Nearly 25 centimetres (10 inches) of rain fell in just a few hours.

Consistently the wettest spot in the world is Mount Wai-ale-ale in the Hawaiian islands, where the average rainfall is around 1,500 centimetres (410 inches)! This is perhaps less surprising when you consider it can rain on up to 350 days a year. On the other hand the town of Arica, on the Chilean side of the Chile-Peru border, has one of the lowest average rainfalls, with around 8.5 millimetres (a third of an inch) falling annually.

2 Snow

Snowflakes are fascinating objects and, like fingerprints, no two are ever the same. The different forms they can take – prisms, needles, plates or stars – depend on the temperature, altitude and the saturation of the clouds as they form. Flakes themselves are not individual crystals but collections of crystals that link up as they fall. They join together when they are wet and then re-freeze, so it is the case that we tend to find larger flakes where the temperatures are relatively high, i.e. only just below freezing. This type of snow not only produces the biggest flakes, but also often the heaviest falls. This is because in warmer weather the air can contain more moisture and thus, to put it crudely, more raw

Snow crystals.

material with which to make the snow.

Many people say it is the smaller, more powdery snow which is more dangerous, as it is likely to settle longer. This may be true, in so far as such snow is produced when temperatures are lower and is therefore less likely to melt than the recently fallen snow. Another important point is the nature of the snow once it has fallen. The snow we get tends to be wet and in large flakes. This means it sticks together and is much harder to clear with the snow blower which is so effective with powdery snow in colder climates.

An expression sometimes heard is that the weather is 'too cold' for snow. But we only have to consider the massive snow falls in really cold spots such as Scandinavia and Alaska to see this cannot be true. However, it is fair to say that we have the coldest weather in clear conditions at night and that cloud cover – perhaps bringing snow – causes the temperature to rise.

The highest recorded snowfall was at Paradise, Mount Rainier in the United States, in the year 1971-1972, when a staggering 31.1 metres (102 feet) of snow fell!

The intermediary stage, when some of the falling flakes have melted but the precipitation hits the ground as half-snow and half-rain, is what we call *sleet*. More dangerous by far is the rare but treacherous freezing rain. Here the water droplets are super-cooled, which means they can exist as water below 0°C (32°F). However, once they hit a freezing surface they freeze instantly, bringing chaos to roads and buildings. In a three-day spell in January 1940 freezing rain brought down telegraph wires and trees; there were even reports of birds dying in mid-flight in the horrific conditions. Such conditions can be deadly at sea, when the weight of ice builds up to the point where ships become top heavy and capsize.

3 Hail

Hail is another fascinating form of precipitation, quite distinct from snow. If you cut a hailstone in half, you find a layered effect rather like the skins of an onion. This is an indication of the curious way in which a hailstone is created.

The stone begins life as an ice crystal in an unstable cloud, such as a cumulonimbus or storm cloud. Strong vertical air currents toss the ice particle up and down within the cloud, gathering alternate layers of frost and ice with each trip. Indeed, the number of journeys made by the stone can be accurately estimated simply by counting the number of layers it contains. Eventually, the hailstone becomes so heavy even the mighty storm cloud cannot hold onto it, and the stone falls to the earth.

Hailstones are typically about 5 millimetres (one-fifth of an inch) in diameter but even ones this size need speeds of around 30 metres (100 feet) a second to keep them suspended in the cloud. Far higher speeds must have been needed to help form the hailstone that fell in the state of Kansas in 1970. It weighed 765 grams (27 ounces) and measured 43.68 centimetres (17.2 inches) in circumference. Though not commonplace, it is not unusual to find hailstones the size of golf balls. Since their formation occurs in storm clouds, hailstones are often associated with violent downpours and storms.

While their formation is certainly fascinating, hailstones are not welcomed in many parts of the world. In one section of the middle of the United States, known as Hail Alley, hail causes millions of pounds worth of damage to crops each year. Acre upon acre of crops can be flattened into a worthless heap by just one downpour.

In the Soviet Union, where farmers are also plagued with the problem, they fire rockets into potential hail clouds, trying to release thousands of tiny particles inside them. The hope is that these particles will form the nuclei of many small hailstones,

Giant hailstone that fell over Kansas, USA in 1970.
National Centre for Atmospheric Research, USA/Science Photo Library

thereby reducing the overall size of the stones and minimizing the damage they cause. Italian farmers, afraid for their orange crops, put matting roofs onto scaffold shelters they erect over the trees to keep off the hail.

A curious phenomenon, as yet not fully explained, is the so-called ice *hydrometeor*. This is a large single block of ice falling from the sky unaccompanied by any other icy precipitation. One, weighing nearly 2 kilograms (4.5 pounds), fell near the southern Spanish town of Cordoba in 1929, while a cubic metre of ice fell near a house in the south-east of England in 1972.

As yet, no one has a watertight explanation for what they are. The theory they all come from aircraft is blown by an instance in 1829 – many years before man learnt to fly! By the same token, these large blocks of ice cannot be classified as hailstones as these always fall in showers. Although rare, these ice blocks clearly pose a real hazard for anyone unfortunate enough to be walking underneath as one falls. And hailstones can be fatal, too. In 1888, 246 people were killed by hail in Moradabad in northern India.

Frost and Dew

This occurs when the temperature drops below 0°C (32°F). It is important to note that temperatures given on weather forecasts are given for the air 2 metres (6.5 feet) above the ground. However, on a clear night the ground will be radiating heat, thus cooling the air closest to it. This means that while the temperature on the ground may be freezing, the temperature 2 metres above the ground could be 2°-3° higher, since air does not conduct heat or heat loss very well.

This variation can be crucial for crop growers and gardeners who want to know whether plants are likely to be hit by a frost or not. This is why you often hear forecasters refer to the possibility of there being a ground frost, even though the chart may not show 0°C (32°F).

The term *hoar frost* is simply used when the air forms ice crystals when cooled below its dew point, giving the characteristic white appearance – indeed a hoar frost can be mistaken at first glance for a fall of snow. Thus the whiteness of a frost does not denote its severity, merely whether there was a great deal of moisture in the air or not. The formation of frost will also depend on the type of surface involved – for example, concrete surfaces will be at a different temperature to grass ones.

A valley floor will also be frostier than its slopes. We hear people talk about 'frost traps' – these are often quite low-lying, sheltered spots where the colder air collects and is undisturbed by a warmer air blowing around. Not the best place for growing early tomatoes!

So-called black ice is another condition often referred to but in reality there is no such thing. Ice is never black. The expression really refers to where a sheet of transparent ice covers the surface of a tarmac road, making it look black and also very hard to spot.

Forecasting road temperatures for local highway authorities has now become a very precise science. Clearly councils do not want to go to the expense of gritting or salting every road if only a few are going to be hit by frost. The Meteorological Office now offers a very detailed service to local authorities combining computer-modelled temperature maps and forecasts.

Dew is formed by the same process as clouds and frost, except that it condenses onto a surface rather than into a cloud. Dew occurs most frequently on a still, clear night when the ground temperature falls fairly quickly causing a small layer of air to cool, condensing the water vapour within it. Dews are particularly heavy during late summer and early autumn when the days are warm but the nights cool quickly.

Winds

The wind is unseen but everywhere – and without it life as we know it could not exist on Earth. It is the wind that distributes the heat more evenly around the planet and drives our weather systems around the world.

Wind is, of course, simply moving air. What is not so simple, however, is the complex pattern of wind movements around the Earth. There are different patterns of winds around the world depending on in which hemisphere and at what latitudes they occur. For example, there are the *trade* winds which blow from the north-east in the northern hemisphere and from the south-east in the southern hemisphere and both sets occur between latitudes 10° and 30°.

In the northern hemisphere we have our own prevailing westerly winds that blow across the Atlantic from the Americas, the pattern and regularity of which is affected by the formation of high and low-pressure areas.

We have all heard the expression about someone or something being in the doldrums. This refers to an area around the equator where the winds are generally non-existent or light and very variable – a nightmare for sailors who became becalmed after the regular trade winds.

Winds are an integral part of our life and environment, so it is no wonder that in many parts of the world regular and identifiable winds have been given names. Few people in Europe have not heard of the *mistral*, a very dry offshore wind blowing along Mediterranean coasts and on occasions a very violent cold wind affecting parts of southern France. The word *monsoon* is now used to describe the extraordinary rainfall which hits part of Asia, but in fact is the name for highly seasonal winds which blow in one direction for part of the year, and the opposite direction for the remainder of the year. The word monsoon itself comes from the Arabic word for 'season'.

Here are some other named winds around the world:
● Berg – A hot dry wind in South Africa coming from the interior.
● Brickfielder – A very hot north-east wind in south-east Australia, blowing during the summer months and carrying dust and sand.

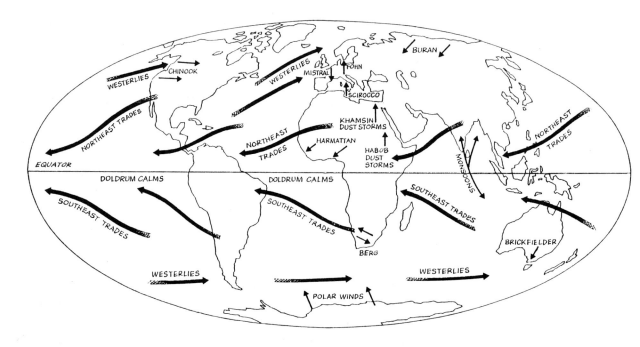

The world's winds.

- Buran – A strong north-easterly affecting parts of the Soviet Union and central Asia, in winter often the harbinger of blizzards.
- Chinook – A lee wind blowing to the east of the Rockies in the United States. It takes its name from a local Indian tribe and is warm and dry, often spelling the end of the winter's snow.
- Föhn – Another dry, warm lee wind. It is the name of the wind coming from the European Alps, but is now used as a generic term for any similar lee wind. It gains its warmth from the air being compressed as it descends down the lee slope of a mountain and historically has been blamed for symptoms such as headaches, depression and even suicide among people living in its path.
- Gregale – A strong wind mainly associated with the cool season in the south and central Mediterranean, blowing from the north-east.
- Habob – A sandstorm wind in northern Sudan, most common in the afternoon or evening. From the Arabic *Haab*, to blow.
- Harmattan – A dry, cool wind from the north-east or east in north-west Africa. Although it carries dust, on occasions sufficient to cause thick hazes, its welcome coolness has earned it the nickname 'doctor' in its tropical home.
- Helm – An English wind, strong, gusty and cold, blowing from the north-east onto the western slopes of the Crossfell range in Cumbria. Particularly common in late winter and spring, it leaves a thick bank of cloud about the range, called 'the helm'.
- Horse latitudes – Belts of light, variable winds in the sub-tropics at about 35° latitude. So-called because in these becalmed spots sailors used to have to throw overboard their horses dying from thirst.
- Khamsin – A hot, dry southerly wind blowing from the interior of Africa over Egypt. It frequently carries dust and is common in late spring and early summer.
- Levanter – An easterly wind in the Straits of Gibraltar. Strong and common in the summer.
- Leveche – A dry and hot southerly wind in south-east Spain heralding an advancing depression.
- Libeccio – A gusty south-westerly wind in the Mediterranean, commoner in winter.
- Pampero – A very cold south-westerly wind from the Andes sweeping across the *pampas* of Argentina and Uruguay. Often

accompanied by storms and a severe drop in temperature.

• Reshabar – A very gusty, strong wind, blowing north-easterly in southern Kurdistan. Dry and warm in summer, cold in winter.

• Seistan – A very strong summer wind from the north in eastern Iran, known as the 'wind of 120 days' as it lasts about four months. Can reach hurricane force and carries dust.

• Shamal – Another summer wind, a north-westerly, blowing over Iraq and the Persian Gulf. Normally decreases at night, and is hot and dry.

• Simoon – A short-lived wind in the Arabic deserts, hot and oppressive, often causing the body to overheat because one cannot perspire quickly enough. Can appear as a whirlwind carrying dust.

• Scirocco – A southerly wind in the Mediterranean which near North Africa can be very hot and dry, carrying dust. It is moister when it reaches Europe, having picked up water from the Mediterranean.

• Southerly buster – A name given by Australians to sudden changes of wind in the south and south-east of the country. The wind change is normally north-west to south and comes with a sudden drop in temperature.

• Tramontana – A dry cool northerly wind in the Mediterranean.

• Vendavales – Strong, gusty south-westerly winds in the Gibraltar Straits which bring rain and stormy weather.

A different category of wind altogether is the *jet stream*. There are two main jet streams, one in each hemisphere, each one blowing from west to east. Jet streams blow at an altitude of around 10.5 kilometres (35,000 feet), that is at the *tropopause*, the boundary between the *troposphere* in which we live and the *stratosphere* above. They can travel at speeds of up to 480km/h (300mph) and although narrow – just a few hundred miles wide – can stretch half way around the globe in length. Although the jet streams are very high it should not be supposed they have no impact on our weather on the ground. On the contrary, in the northern hemisphere the jet stream has a massive impact on the formation of high and low-pressure zones and thus greatly influences our weather. The jet streams were only discovered in the last war, when pilots crossing the Atlantic east to west found them a slowing influence.

The effect that winds can have on our lives was graphically illustrated in Britain in October 1987 when hurricane-force winds uprooted 15 million trees and caused widespread damage. Winds of a similar strength were responsible for more than forty deaths across Britain in January 1990. On neither occasion was a *hurricane* responsible. Hurricanes are specific, intense storms, also known as *typhoons*, which do not occur in our climate. What both incidents did have, however, were hurricane-force winds according to the definition in the *Beaufort Scale* of winds. These are force 12 or more on the scale – winds of more than 118km/h (74mph). They were caused by very intense low-pressure areas which always generate fierce winds.

Apart from the wind's direct effect on land, it also has an impact on the ocean currents of the world, driving such currents as the Gulf Stream. In addition, the wind creates waves on the surfaces of oceans, affecting shipping and also, in the right circumstances, bringing pleasure to surfers.

Wind Speed on the Beaufort Scale

Beaufort Force	Average Mph	Speed Km/h	Description	Observation
0	0	0	Calm	Smoke rises vertically
1	2	3	Light airs	Smoke drifts in the wind
2	5	9	Light breeze	Leaves rustle
3	10	15	Gentle breeze	Leaves and small twigs move constantly. Small flags extended.
4	15	25	Moderate wind	Wind raises dust and loose paper.
5	21	35	Fresh wind	Small trees sway.
6	28	45	Strong wind	Large branches move. Whistling in phone wires. Difficult to use umbrellas.
7	35	56	Very strong wind	Whole trees in motion.
8	43	68	Gale	Twigs break off trees. Difficult to walk.
9	50	81	Severe gale	Chimney pots and slates removed.
10	59	94	Storm	Trees uprooted. Structural damage.
11	69	110	Severe storm	Widespread damage.
12	over 74	over 119	Hurricane	Widespread damage.

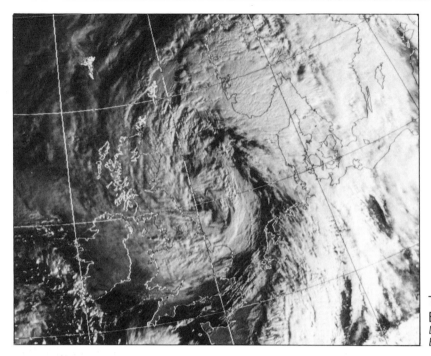

The storm that struck southern England on 16 October 1987.
Department of Electrical Engineering and Electronics, University of Dundee.

Hurricanes

A hurricane is one of the most destructive elements in nature. The name is of Spanish/Caribbean-Portuguese origin and means big wind' – a fair description for something which can generate winds of around 160km/h (100mph) and can wreak havoc and destruction on anything unfortunate enough to lie in its path.

Hurricanes form in several parts of the world, although they are known by different names – *typhoons* in the West Pacific and *cyclones* in the Bay of Bengal. Hurricanes contain ferocious power and need energy to develop and then sustain themselves – fortunately they are not everyday occurrences.

To form, a hurricane needs warm water, normally not less than 27°C (80°F), which explains why they do not occur in our home waters. When a disturbance occurs in the atmosphere in the tropics, an upward draught may be created, pulling up with it warm moist air. This then condenses as rain, releasing further latent heat energy to help fuel the developing hurricane which continues to feed off the cyclical process, growing in size and strength. Rather like the low-pressure systems with which we are familiar, winds begin circulating at great speeds around a central point, known as the eye. At the eye itself, all is calm.

Hurricanes are typically about 480 kilometres (300 miles) in diameter and form within 1,600 kilometres (1,000 miles) of the equator. They generally move westwards at speeds of around 16km/h (10mph), and may then move up to threaten Caribbean islands or even the east coast of the United States – often with devastating effect.

As we have seen they can only form at sea, where the conditions are right. When they reach a sizeable land mass they will gradually blow themselves out as they lack the fuel to keep on self-generating. This explains why most of the damage caused by hurricanes in the United States is in coastal regions.

As well as the murderous winds, hurricanes can deposit vast amounts of rain. In 1928 a hurricane deposited 76 centimetres (30 inches) of rain over the mountains of Puerto Rico; some typhoons are said to have brought 1 metre (40 inches) of rain in one day. The Philippines, for example, received 116 centimetres (46 inches) in a single day in 1911! The power and ferocity of the winds can flatten whole villages, uproot all but the sturdiest of trees and cause huge waves which swamp coastal dwellings. Given this it is little wonder that a great deal of attention is given, especially in the United States, to hurricane detection and to the possibility of reducing their impact. Individual hurricanes can cause up to 1 billion dollars-worth of damage.

Hurricanes are now tracked by satellite where their swirling mass around a central spot is readily apparent. Unfortunately, it is still difficult to forecast their exact path. The key to a storm's strength appears to be in the size of the eye – the larger the eye, the weaker the surrounding winds. Experiments are now in progress to see whether by dropping salt, ice or silver iodine to seed cloud in the hurricane another eye can be created. The theory is that this second eye could join with the original, creating a larger one with a consequent reduction of wind speeds. There is, however, always the danger that an increase of rain may only serve to add to the fuelling of the hurricane and expand rather than reduce its destructive power.

Rather endearingly, hurricanes are always given human names – Flora, Betsy and so on. The practice was started by an Australian called Clement Wragge who lived at the end of the last century. A slightly vindictive nature led him to call the storms after people whom he disliked! Until the 1970s all hurricanes were, rather unfairly, named after women. Then equality took over and they are now alternated between male and female names, as witnessed by the recent Hurricane Gilbert.

Tornadoes

Although much smaller than hurricanes, tornadoes are, if anything, even more destructive. They may measure from just a few metres across to 500 metres (1,625 feet) in diameter but wind speeds can reach anything up to 320km/h (200mph) inside. It is, however, impossible to be sure as any wind gauge is wrecked by the power of a tornado.

Tornadoes are generally associated with the United States, where there is a 'tornado alley' running from Texas to Illinois, and that is certainly where the largest and most ferocious of this phenomena occur. But the British Isles has also suffered them, for example in 1971 when a tornado lifted a 90-ton railway engine more than 30 metres (100 feet) along a railway line in south Yorkshire. Two years later a tornado ripped the roofs off laboratory buildings at Cranfield in Bedfordshire.

However, it is in the United States where the most spectacular examples occur. In 1917 a Texan tornado travelled 471 kilometres (293 miles), while in 1931 an 83-ton railway carriage with 117 passengers was lifted in the air and then deposited in a ditch.

Tornadoes begin their life as a tunnel projecting down from

Tornado seen from a helicopter over Vietnam.
F. W. Lane

the base of a cloud, often a thundercloud. If the conditions are right, for example violent updraughts, the characteristic spin can develop and the full-fledged tornado is born. Unlike hurricanes, tornadoes can move quite quickly, at speeds of up to 120km/h (75mph), making them a hazardous prospect to track down, though they can also remain stationary for many minutes. As the tornado moves across the ground the storm funnel does not always reach down to the surface, as shown by the pattern of damage it leaves behind it – some areas are left quite untouched. It almost seems as if the funnel of cloud needs to lift off the ground occasionally to rejuvenate itself.

Many people have seen something of the destructive power of a tornado in the opening sequence of *The Wizard of Oz*, the film starring Judy Garland. The damage is caused in four ways:

(1) The sheer power of the wind which can cause great devastation.

(2) The rotation of the funnel cloud which, because of its powerful twisting effect, can pull off the tops of trees or uproot whole trees themselves.

(3) The tornado can cause a kind of explosion. At the centre of a tornado the pressure is much lower than normal, perhaps as low as 500 millibars, or half a normal atmosphere. So when one moves towards a building the air inside the building, which is at a much higher pressure, bursts out – literally causing the building to explode in an effort to equalize the pressure. For this reason, householders in the path of a tornado are told to open windows and doors so that the pressure can escape more gradually and less damagingly.

(4) The sheer lifting power of the tornado. People and property can be literally lifted upwards by the suction of the updraught within the tornado and carried great distances. Among these reports are remarkable accounts of people being sucked away by a tornado, only to be planted, quite gently, back on the ground thanks to a brief reduction in the force of the wind.

It is interesting to note at this point that throughout history, and including recent times, there have been reports of strange objects falling from the sky, such as frogs, flocks of geese, goldfish and tadpoles – and even on one occasion crosses! It seems likely that these are all objects which have been sucked up by a tornado, carried for some distance, then dropped *en masse* as the tornado weakened, causing understandable consternation to the people below.

Tornadoes are awesome sights, black with menace as they approach. They also sound quite frightening, likened by some to the sound of a squadron of jet aircraft. There are several hundred tornadoes reported each year in the United States, and doubtless others in uninhabited areas that go unseen.

One theory suggests that the number of tornadoes has increased this century, and some have claimed that this could be linked to the activity of sunspots, which are known to be connected in some way to weather patterns on Earth.

In the United States warning forecasts are given about the possible development of tornadoes and radar is now used to detect them as they develop early on. In addition, the Torro Tornado Intensity Scale has been developed to give people an idea of the expected severity of an approaching tornado rather as our own shipping forecasts give warning of storm levels at seas. The scale runs from 0-12:

Abbreviated version:

Torro force	Tornado description	Likely damage
FC	funnel cloud, start of tornado	movement in treetops, no damage except tops of tall towers
O	light	twigs snap, tents etc affected, litter sent spiralling
1	mild	planks etc lifted up, small trees uprooted, chimney pots removed
2	moderate	roofs damaged, big branches torn off, visible tornado path in crops
3	strong	roofs stripped of tiles, trees uprooted, doors and windows damaged
4	severe	roofs torn off, trees twisted apart
5	intense	one-ton cars lifted, trees carried through air
6	moderately devastating	cars over one ton carried through air, weak buildings collapse
7	strongly devastating	trains overturned, steel-framed buildings buckle
8	severely devastating	most houses collapse, cars thrown some distance
9	severely devastating	trains hurled about
10	intensely devastating	frame and wooden homes hurled from foundations
11	intensely devastating	steel-reinforced concrete buildings severely damaged.
12	super tornadoes	steel-reinforced concrete buildings severely damaged.

In addition to land tornadoes there is a marine variety known as the *waterspout*, a phenomenon often mistaken for a sea monster in past times. It needs warm water to develop, and is thus rarer in our waters, and does not become as intense as its land cousin. However, despite providing an impressive sight it can be a hazard to small boats, particularly when the spout starts to disintegrate and gallons of water come crashing down.

Thunder and lightning

Thunderstorms, which produce thunder and lightning, are the most dramatic and powerful weather phenomena we see in this country. They occur when moist, warm air rises quickly and unchecked forming the characteristic storm cloud – the cumulonimbus.

Such conditions can come about in two ways. After a long hot spell in summer, there is moist humid air around; this begins to rise, heated by the warm weather. When this big bubble of air forms cloud, the makings of a summer thunderstorm have begun. Another way is when, on a cold front, a mass of cold air forces moist warm air to rise sharply upwards, creating the same effect.

Electrical charges are present in all clouds, positive and negative. In the thunderclouds there is massive turbulence, strong updraughts and currents, swirling the charged particles around. In such circumstances, with ice, water droplets and water vapour all present, a massive positive differential begins to build up at the top of the cloud, while a large negative charge develops on the bottom of the cloud.

At high altitudes this large differential may be 'satisfied' by a lightning discharge between the different parts of the cloud. This takes the form of a fork, hence the term *fork lightning* – but because it is shielded from the ground by clouds we see it as a flash of *sheet lightning*. However, if the cloud is closer to the ground then the negatively charged section of the cloud may interact with the ground, which is normally positively charged. A lightning stroke from the cloud forms a path down towards the ground, seeking the path of least resistance and forming the familiar zig-zag pattern of fork lightning. What we actually see as the fork lightning is the *return* stroke from the positively charged Earth to the cloud. This stroke may contain up to 100 million volts and its enormous power disrupts the air particles, causing the thunder clap which we hear a short time after witnessing the lightning. This return stroke to the cloud, which may create a temperature of up to 25,000°C (45,000°F), follows the same path as the downwards stroke.

One comforting result from this is that if you are out in a thunderstorm and see a stroke of lightning, you know you have missed it! Lightning looks for the quickest path to the ground, which is why tall, exposed buildings such as churches, or skyscrapers, and trees get more than their fair share of strikes. If you are caught out in such a storm it is best to avoid sheltering under an isolated tall tree; in fact you are rather safer in a car. You are normally safe indoors though a wise precaution is to unplug electrical items from their sockets. And take heart – people have been hit by lightning and lived to tell the tale – sometimes more than once.

Lightning around the Eiffel Tower in Paris.

Another phenomenon associated with electrical storms is *St Elmo's Fire*. It is not a fire as such, but greenish or white light that emanates from elevated objects like the masts of ships, weather vanes, lightning conductors or from the wing tips or propellers of aircraft in flight. It is caused by a 'brush' discharge of electricity near an electrical storm.

Optical Effects

The best known of these is the rainbow, which gets an early mention in the Bible, in the Book of Genesis, as a part of God's covenant with Man after the flood and the saga of Noah's Ark. Many legends have sprung up around the rainbow, not least that there is a crock of gold waiting at the end of one. This, also, will never be tested as it is not possible to get near a rainbow. They are simply an optical effect. Rainbows are caused by the sun's rays passing through raindrops and being bent – or refracted – by the process, causing the white light to split into its constituent parts – red, orange, yellow, green, blue, indigo and violet. To see a rainbow, the observer has to be standing between the sun and the rain. The best examples are seen in the morning or early evening, when the sun is low in the sky, and we see virtually a full semicircle. A few lucky air travellers, given the right conditions, have been able to witness the rare sight of a rainbow in a full circle, where there is no ground to get in the way.

Mirages are another well-known if less commonly observed optical effect. There are in fact two types of mirages: the *inferior* mirage and the *superior* mirage. The inferior mirage is the one seen typically by the desert traveller, desperate for water, who sees what he thinks is an inviting pool ahead of him, only to discover that it is not actually there. This is caused by the fact that light travels at a different speed through hot air than through cold air. So, in somewhere like a desert, or above a tarmac road on a summer's day, light rays coming down from the sky hit the much hotter air above the ground and are bent upwards to our eyes, giving us an image of the skyline which may well have the appearance of rippling water.

In a superior mirage the effect is reversed. Where the air next to the ground is colder than the air above, in polar regions for instance, light from an image beneath the horizon is bent downwards towards us giving us a view of, say, a mountain range, beneath the horizon before we can really 'see' it.

Forecasting

Early Forecasting

Man has always been greatly influenced by the weather. From the earliest stages of our development on the planet the climate has been crucial in determining supplies of flora and fauna, the type of shelter needed, the presence or otherwise of water – in short our very survival. Of course the longer-term effects of climate, such as overall cooling or warming of the planet, have by and large happened sufficiently gradually for man to adapt naturally to them.

However, the year-by-year and day-by-day fluctuations in the weather have always been apparent to people; and equally apparent has been the need to be able to forecast them.

In more primitive times, when our forebears relied on hunting and living off the land, people lived much closer to nature and had an instinctive awareness of the weather around them. They could 'sense' approaching changes and read the natural signs. Nowadays, in our high-tech society where most people in the west live in towns and cities, we have largely lost touch with this basic weather sense; only on the occasions when the weather 'misbehaves' as in violent storms or snowfalls do we become more sensitive to it. Perhaps now only the sailors and farmers – and cricket groundsmen! – still learn to read the signs in this way. Just as old as forecasting, however, is scepticism about how effective it can be. As an old Scottish rhyme puts it:

'To talk of the weather is nothing but folly;
When it rains on the hill the sun shines in the valley.'

That is a salutary reminder to any forecaster!

From the earliest times people linked the cycles of stars and heavenly bodies with weather patterns on Earth. The comings and goings of constellations in the night sky were used to forecast the cycle of the seasons which could be of such importance in determining food supplies, especially in temperate mid-latitudes, like our own, where there is a fixed and quite marked difference between the seasons. In Egypt, early astronomers looked for the movement of the Dogstar Sirius to herald the all-important flood and drought seasons associated with their lifeline, the River Nile. Indeed an early reference to forecasting can be found in the Book of Genesis. Joseph was asked

Opposite: Giant waterspout seen in the Bermuda Triangle area.
J. G. Golden/Science Photo Library

Above: Sunshine recorder in high latitudes
Steve Weston

Right: Radarnet image illustrating the development and movement of rain over Southern England and Wales.
Crown copyright

Opposite top: Aurora borealis, the Northern Lights, photographed over spruce trees near Fairbanks, Alaska.
Jack Finch/Science Photo Library

Opposite bottom: Shallow fog developing over the Thames Valley near Henley-on-Thames
J. F. P. Galvin

Following pages: Sunset photographed over Wigston, Leicestershire, on 12 September 1987.
B. K. Wood.

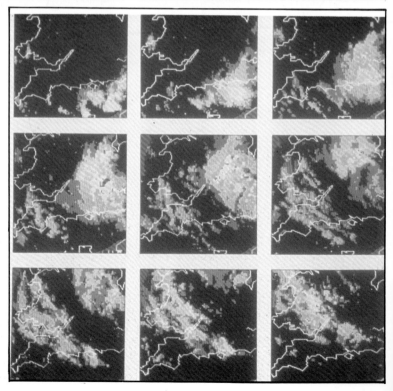

Above: Frost fair held on the Thames in 1814.

Left: Rainbow
Phil Jude/Science Photo Library

Opposite top: Thermal springs at Waiotapu, North Island, New Zealand.
Doug Allan/Science Photo Library

Opposite bottom: Irisation in Cirrocumulus clouds photographed over Lawford Heath, Rugby, 13 January 1979.
S. D. Burt

by the pharaoh to interpret some strange dreams he had had involving seven cows and seven heads of grain. Joseph replied:

'Seven years of great abundance are coming throughout the land of Egypt, but seven years of famine will follow. Then all the abundance in Egypt will be forgotten and the famine will ravage the land.'

It is at least possible this was based on the Nile's known fourteen-year cycle of flooding and drought.

However, following the cycle of the seasons and long-term patterns was of no real help in predicting the more immediate future such as impending storms or hurricanes. Man began to observe more closely the various phenomena of nature and use them as signs of approaching weather changes. Such phenomena as red skies in the evening, haloes around the moon and the feeding patterns of birds were observed and used as the basis of predictions. Often such observations became enshrined in folklore and sayings passed from generation to generation, first by word of mouth and then written down. As I discuss in a separate chapter on weather lore, many of these sayings are hopelessly vague or downright wrong, but some were based on well-founded observations and at least gave some degree of forecasting. For example, the presence of a halo effect around the sun or moon can often mean that bad weather is on the way. Hence the old saying of the Zuni Indians: 'The moon, if in house be, cloud it will, rain soon will come.' Together with sayings, myths and legends of pagan gods became part of the cultural tradition of weather. It is not hard to see why the weather, such a vital part of life, was thought by early man to be controlled by divine forces. The sun, moon, wind, thunder and rain all had their deities. Sacrifices were made to the weather gods, in an attempt to bring favourable weather for crops or war. Unusual events like an eclipse of the sun were often seen as signs of disapproval in heaven and thus required a sacrifice to make good the imagined wrong.

The Old Testament story of the Great Flood and God's warning to Noah that allowed his escape in the Ark is echoed in the mythology of other cultures. Elsewhere in the world, in India for example, attempts were made thousands of years ago to predict such things as the monsoon by recording weather effects in previous months. Centuries before the birth of Christ, the Chinese developed a calendar divided into twenty-four different

Opposite: Sunrise over Shillingstone, Dorset, on 21 September 1989.
M. Nimmo

weather periods with instructions to farmers when crops should be sown and harvested, and so forth. If the actual weather did not coincide with the weather period, the farmer would then adjust his plans accordingly.

In the west, the emergence of the Greek and then the Roman civilizations gradually brought a more rational and less superstitious approach to the weather. The Greek philosopher, Aristotle, produced a work, *Meteorologica*, which was for centuries the accepted wisdom on all matters concerning the theory of weather, though it did not concentrate on forecasting. Later, two Roman scholars, Pliny and Ptolemy, produced treatises on weather which incorporated all the existing theories of the time. However, although the Greeks and Romans had begun recorded observations of the weather, there was still no system for producing accurate predictions based on empirical evidence, that is to say, predictions based on observed weather phenomena. And when Europe slipped into the so-called Dark Ages, at the demise of the Roman civilization, there was little real progress in producing new ways of predicting the weather. Thus in medieval Europe, weather forecasting was a complete mix of observations of natural phenomena, folklore and astrological divinations, with the work of Aristotle still underpinning the philosophy of weather study. The rise of 'quack' weather forecasting became widespread with numerous treatises and predictions written in Latin and based on the movements of the planets and stars.

In particular, the moon became important as an apparent foreteller of the weather, and its movements and appearances were studied avidly. Much folklore was based on the moon, including the old proverb 'Pale moon doth rain, Red moon doth blow, White moon doth neither rain nor snow.' During the Middle Ages wild predictions also began about the advent of natural catastrophes supposedly gleaned from the study of the planets and stars. One of the worst was the prediction in Europe by an astrologer, Johannes of Toledo, that winds and famine would bring disaster to the continent in 1186. Needless to say, nothing of the sort happened, but astonishingly such dramatic predictions remained popular for hundreds of years, well into the 19th century, and there was a tremendous growth in almanacs full of lurid but vague forecasts. Occasionally someone would get it right – and this only served to increase the esteem in which such predictions were held. One example occurred in

1838 when the *Weather Almanac* correctly predicted that 20 January would be the coldest day of the winter – in fact it was the coldest day of the century in London! This success meant the almanac was quickly sold out and winter became known as Murphy's Winter after the author, Patrick Murphy, who made a small fortune from the sales!

The Origins of Modern Forecasting

Despite the occasional success of astrological-based predictions, such an approach led down a dead end in the search for a reliable and practical means of forecasting the weather.

A problem for those of a rational disposition in the Middle Ages, men like the 14th-century scientist, Nicole Oresme, who realized the need for a coherent framework of rules, was that scientific development was stunted by the belief that the Earth was at the centre of the universe. It was only when Galileo and Copernicus, propounding their theory of the Earth revolving around the sun, were able to break free from these shackles, that the development of new thought in meteorology really began. From the early 1600s there was an explosion of interest in scientific observation and measuring of the weather. To a certain extent this was because of the increase in long-distance sailing, to the New World, which focused people's minds on weather and forecasts. Indeed, from that point of view, the observations made by sailors in their logs have been of great value as sources of meteorological information. In 1600 the first thermometer was developed and the early barometer followed in 1643. The Italian, Evangelista Torricelli, developed it using mercury, though the French scientist, Blaise Pascal, later repeated the experiment using red wine instead of mercury.

This dawning of a new age of science happened internationally and by the mid-17th century meteorologists were trying to establish a network of co-ordinated observations across Europe. In 1660 the German physicist and mayor of Magdeburg, Otto von Guericke, became the first person to use a barometer to forecast weather when he predicted a bad storm. It was von Guericke who also demonstrated the strength of atmospheric pressure when in a public experiment he took two metal hemispheres, fixed them together and pumped out all the air to create a vacuum. A team of sixteen horses could not pull the hemispheres apart!

Further attempts were made to establish a system of coordinating weather observations taken at different spots at the same time, including a British project in the early 18th century to get observations from Europe, North America and India. This approach led to an important discovery by the French scientist, De Borda, who found that the variations in pressures from site to site were closely related to the wind velocity. This was the first inkling that low and high-pressure areas moved around as weather systems – a feature which is now familiar to us from the images presented in television weather forecast charts.

By the 1780s France had established a network of some seventy observation stations at home and in various parts of Europe, and the great scientist, Antoine Lavoisier, wanted to create a network all over the world. Meanwhile from Mannheim in Germany spread a similar network, while smaller systems were developing in Britain and North America.

By the early 19th century, although scientists had a much more detailed understanding of how weather worked thanks to the growth in detailed observations, meteorologists were still unable to forecast from such data. This was because of the inevitable time lapse involved in collecting all the information centrally – by the time the information was passed on by letter it was too late to prepare a forecast. This changed after Samuel Morse, from whom the Morse Code takes its name, developed the telegraph system in the 1830s. This revolutionary system meant that weather data could be collected from a number of stations and analysed on the day it was observed. By 1848, daily weather reports were appearing in the *Daily News* in London based on information transmitted from weather stations at 9am that same day. In the United States, newspapers also began publishing daily weather reports. Meanwhile the disastrous failure to predict the storm of 14 November 1854, which decimated the British fleet at Balaclava, sent alarm bells ringing through officialdom and prompted increased interest in developing more comprehensive, or synoptic, weather forecasts. Under Admiral Robert FitzRoy the new Meteorological Department of the Board of Trade was charged with the prediction of storms and started producing three-day forecasts. By the 1870s, forecasts were being produced for other government departments and newspapers. Similar organizations were set up around the world, including those in France, Germany and the United States, as other developments occurred.

Register map showing atmospheric conditions for 9am on September 17, 1851, collected at the Great Exhibition.
Trustees of the Science Museum.

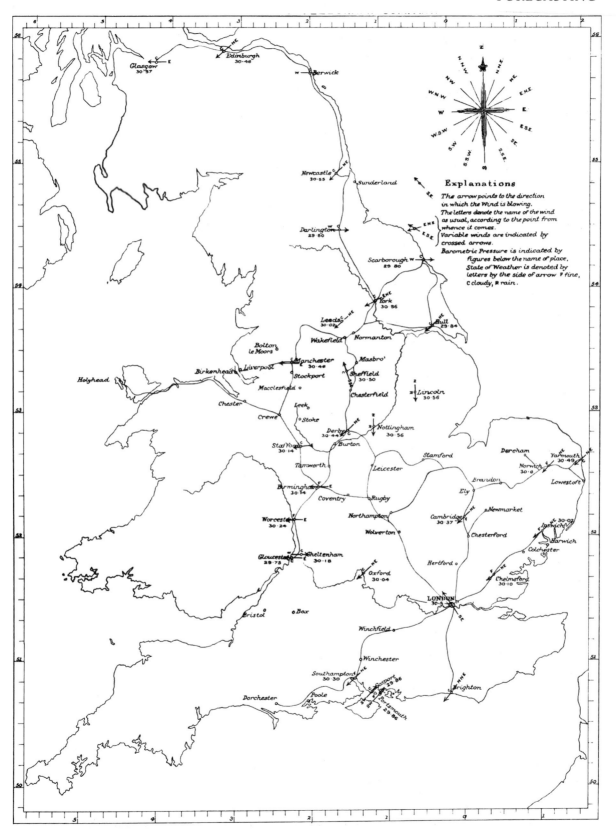

Explanations

The arrow points to the direction
in which the Wind is blowing.
The letters denote the name of the wind
as usual, according to the point from
whence it comes.
Variable winds are indicated by
crossed arrows.
Barometric Pressure is indicated by
figures below the name of place,
State of Weather is denoted by
letters by the side of arrow F fine,
C cloudy, R rain.

The isobar, a line joining up points of equal pressure, started to be used on weather charts and this assisted in the analysis of such charts. Although the accuracy and quantity of observations had improved greatly, meteorologists still had no information on what was happening in the upper atmosphere. At the end of the 19th century this deficiency was made good when the first meteorological instruments were sent up into the atmosphere on balloons and kites. These were forerunners of the radiosondes which are still an important feature of gathering information in modern meteorology. The development of these upper-atmosphere measurements have given forecasters an extra vertical dimension to their weather models.

Another leap forward in forecasting techniques came from Norway early in the 20th century, where the Norwegian meteorologist, Vilhelm Bjerknes, set up the Bergen Geophysical Institute and more detailed analysis of weather charts and models was carried out. Hence models were produced showing how low-pressure systems develop, mature and then decay according to general principles, and this helped a great deal in forecasting how various weather systems would develop. The concept of air masses, which certainly in our own latitudes can combine to form low-pressure areas, was also developed. With more and better upper-atmosphere measurements being taken after the First World War, a much more comprehensive picture of the atmosphere began to be developed by meteorologists. By the time of the Second World War, forecasting techniques had been constantly refined and by the 1950s perhaps had reached the limits of their ability to predict the weather. The great skill of forecasters was especially important in analysing charts and extrapolating how weather systems would develop. However, earlier in the century mathematical techniques had been developed which were later to revolutionize the way in which forecasts were carried out, and they formed the basis of the forecasting we have today.

The story of modern numerical forecasting is the story of two men. The first was someone I mentioned earlier, the Norwegian Bjerknes, who came up with the idea of applying hydrodynamic principles to weather charts, that is applying basic laws of physics to explain the dynamics of weather systems. This idea was taken up before the First World War by an English mathematician, L.F. Richardson, who eventually published his results in 1922 under the title *Weather Prediction by Numerical*

Dr. L. F. Richardson.

Process. This was a seminal work in its approach to weather forecasting, but unfortunately for him Richardson was a man ahead of his time. His system involved expressing physical laws of atmospheric dynamics as mathematical equations and then using observational data fed in from weather stations to predict how weather systems would develop. But the amount of computation needed for this system was far beyond the scope of a human forecaster. It was only after the Second World War, when computers were developed, that the numerical approach could be adopted, initially in the United States. Since then the technique has been broadly the same, though more sophisticated weather models have been used which have allowed more detailed forecasts. The dawn of the satellite age has allowed the nations of the world to get together and adopt a global approach to weather forecasting and analysis. In 1968 the World Weather Watch was set up with the co-operation of all the members of the World Meteorological Organization. Under this system, there is global transference of weather data worldwide thus improving the forecasts of all member countries.

Long-Range Forecasts

The need for longer-term predictions of the weather has increased interest in developing long-range forecasts. However, to date they have not been anywhere near as successful as the usually reliable week-long ones produced by national meteorological offices.

In modern times, such forecasting began when Benjamin Franklin, the 18th-century American scientist and statesman, speculated that a particularly cold winter may have been caused by volcanic eruptions shielding the Earth from sunlight. The discovery last century of permanent or semi-permanent pressure systems, such as the high-pressure zone lurking to our west near the Azores, helped build up a picture that assisted in developing longer-term forecasts. Nowadays, long-range forecasters make use of statistics to discover past patterns that may be of use in predicting future trends. Increasingly important is the study of ocean temperatures, now seen as crucial in helping to shape our weather. The oceans, with their store of heat in the form of relatively warm water, provide much of the energy that drives our weather systems.

Despite strenuous attempts around the world to refine techniques, reliable predictions have still been difficult to reach, especially in changeable weather zones such as our own. The Meteorological Office, also referred to as the Met Office, has now abandoned the public long-range predictions, though specialized and tailor-made ones are available as part of their commercial services.

The Business of Forecasting

Meteorologists have long realized that the many and varied weather phenomena of the world are intimately connected and form a part of one giant, and still not fully understood, whole. In one sense it can be likened to a kind of three-dimensional jigsaw puzzle. Forecasting, no less than any other branch of meteorology, has to take account of this and consequently modern forecasting is based on information gathered from all over the world. The 160 members of the World Meteorological Organization collect information and feed it through regional centres, of which Bracknell is one, into the three world meteorological centres at Melbourne, Moscow and Washington. Here vast computers process information gathered from all parts of the globe and then feed this back to the regional centres which in turn prepare detailed analyses for passing on to national meteorological centres every six hours. (It can be seen from this that Bracknell performs a dual role as both a regional and a national centre.) To make such rapid computer communications work smoothly all such transmissions are carried out in an internationally agreed code. Of course, at the same time as a centre like Bracknell is receiving weather data from around the world, it is also sending out information from its observation centres into the shared pool of data.

Once the information arrives at Bracknell it is fed into a computer which allocates data like temperature, wind speed, pressure and humidity to a grid reference. This is not restricted to surface level but is taken at fifteen different levels in the atmosphere to increase the sophistication and accuracy of the model. At the upper levels there are fewer observations and so in the 'gaps' the computer interpolates its own data. Once this is stored, the computer applies the information about pressure, temperatures and wind speed to mathematical equations to describe what the atmosphere is going to be like. It is then able to draw up weather charts showing predictions of what the temperature, pressure, rainfall and so forth will be like and how these will develop.

Computer operating room at the
Met Office headquarters,
Bracknell.
Crown copyright

However, although the ability of the computer to forecast is highly regarded, the machine is not left entirely to its own devices. At Bracknell for example, the senior forecaster, assisted by a team of experts, checks what the computer is producing. One expert may be analysing the plotted change over the next four to five days, another analysing the dynamics of the upper atmosphere. The aim of this is to check that the computer is working along the right lines before the numerically based weather patterns are sent by computer line to the various weather centres for detailed local interpretation.

At the London Weather Centre, where our national radio forecasts are prepared, the senior forecaster will take the numerical forecast he has received from Bracknell as the basis for his own forecast. But he will still get out his pencil and rubber and draw up charts. He will be looking at what the numerical model has predicted and will compare this with what is actually happening in terms of the weather, in case there is a conflict.

The senior forecaster will draw up what are called 'surface

charts', that is those based on the observations taken at ground or sea level. In the British Isles these are drawn up and analysed every hour. The observations of cloud and rain will assist him in detecting the activity of weather fronts, as will the use of satellite pictures. The charts for the upper air are produced less frequently, perhaps every six or twelve hours. It is the relationship between what is happening in the upper air and on the surface that is crucial in dictating the formation of weather systems.

I think it is important to stress at this point that, despite the huge reliance placed on computers, the skill of the human forecaster is still essential in producing good, reliable forecasts. It is the human forecaster who is still the expert at predicting the weather in the very short term, say six to twelve hours ahead, while the computer model becomes more useful after that period. And the computer cannot, as the human can, take into account all the geographical quirks of local areas which may have a significant effect on the weather. For example, it would not be able to predict that the wind speed at Plymouth in Devon may be at 80km/h (50mph) while just a few miles up the coast at Berry Head, Brixham, the gusts could reach 144km/h (90mph), as the wind blows straight up the cliff face. This is the advantage of having forecasters in the various weather centres who know their areas well.

An example of how local knowledge can be helpful is seen with farmers. They will listen to general forecasts, especially the farming forecasts, but they will also know from years of experience that a particular hill or valley near their land will affect the type of weather they will have. Such amateur forecasters can often be quite accurate over a short period of around two to six hours.

What the professional forecaster is doing, essentially, is 'fine tuning' the predictions he is being given by the computer. Occasionally the computer, perhaps working on insufficient data – one of the biggest problems in forecasting – will get it wrong, and the forecaster will have to spot this and rely on his own skills. Indeed, at Bracknell there is a group of meteorologists known as the 'intervention team' whose sole job it is to spot errors and correct them. For example, if a hurricane has developed much more quickly and more violently than expected in the Gulf of Mexico the computer model, working on figures from some hours before, will not be able to take this into account when it produces its prediction of how the weather will develop. So a forecaster will add in a bogus observation from a non-existent weather ship. This will allow the computer to adjust its prediction.

One area where the computer may not always be entirely accurate is in the timing. It could be that a weather system approaching the British Isles does not arrive as forecast. Later satellite pictures and radar will show the forecaster that the system is arriving, but more slowly than expected, and he will have to amend the daily forecast accordingly. As we say in forecasting, if we tell you it is going to rain it will – if you wait long enough!

One particular problem for the forecaster is predicting exactly where and when showers will occur. Using a combination of the computer model and individual human skills, the forecaster will be able to tell that there *will* be showers, but pinpointing precise locations and timings is still very difficult. Another type of weather hard to forecast with accuracy is fog, which needs certain specific conditions in which to form. Incidentally, one thing the computer model does not do is say how much sunshine there will be. It gives the likely cloud cover but it is up to the forecaster to interpret from this what the sunshine will be like.

Generally speaking the weather computers are very accurate, and can certainly do things the human forecasters cannot do. Working on the dynamics of the atmosphere at fifteen different

Chart plotters at work in the computer laboratory at Bracknell.
Crown copyright

levels, taking into account the jet stream wind at 9,000 metres (30,000 feet) and then predicting what will happen more than a day ahead is mind-boggling for the human forecaster! And it is a brave forecaster these days who will throw out all the computer's predictions and back his own judgement entirely.

The Forecaster

Meteorology is a science, and at times a very complex one. But forecasting is in many ways still an art. Some forecasters seem to have a very natural and instinctive aptitude for analysing the charts and predicting how the weather will develop. Some may be very good at short-term forecasts; others better at determining the weather over a long period.

All the forecasters at the Met Office have had a very thorough training in meteorology and techniques of forecasting. Some joined the Office as science graduates but many were recruited initially as school-leavers with more modest qualifications. They began their careers as weather observers, getting to know the basics of meteorology and often working alongside forecasters. At the same time they studied to gain the higher qualifications necessary for forecasting.

The forecasting training consists essentially of a lengthy formal course, followed by some months of on-the-job training in a forecasting office under close supervision. Even after this, the new forecaster has to work under the guidance of more experienced colleagues for quite a long time; it is normally at least three years from the start of training before a forecaster is allowed to work independently. Anyone interested in becoming a forecaster should note that maths and physics, not geography, are the preferred subjects to study in preparation – they are the subjects on which meteorology is based.

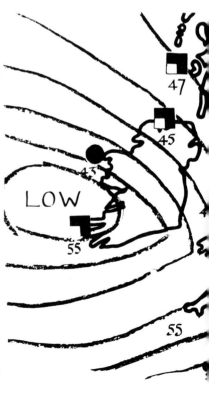

Broadcast Weather Forecasts

The familiar faces of the television broadcasters who regularly invade your living-room bringing the good – or bad – news about the weather are merely the public face of the whole Met Office network. First and foremost they are meteorologists, trained in the usual way, and skilled forecasters in their own right. They become broadcasters after carrying out a variety of jobs in the Met Office. They may have worked on oil rigs, or forecast for the water or electricity boards, or for aviation customers, before becoming part of a unique breed of broadcaster. So how does the transformation to broadcaster occur?

To be chosen from the ranks of the forecasters, the broadcasting weatherman or woman has to pass a voice test. Once they have succeeded they arrive at the London Weather Centre where they are put to work on a variety of jobs. Essentially, they are being trained up as broadcasters and may start their broadcasting careers on local and national radio, both for the BBC and commercial networks.

As a forecaster at a weather centre the use of language is very important, since the main object is to communicate the often complex forecasts produced at Bracknell to the listening public in a language they can understand easily. Most of the radio forecasters write a script for their broadcast, but it has to be written in spoken English, as distinct from written English, so that when read out over the air it sounds natural. Indeed, certain words or phrases are normally used only in written English. The word 'however' is one that is seldom used in the spoken language. The shortening for 'it will' to 'it'll' and many similar abbreviations are often employed in radio scripts as well. The art of reading a script is to make it interesting and make it flow, so that the listener wants to listen to you and to what is being said. You have to tease the audience a little, and not give the whole story away in the first sentence!

Once broadcasters have shown themselves adept on radio, they may be auditioned by the BBC, and if successful they will move over to the headquarters of BBC television at White City in west London where there is a small weather centre and a completely different environment.

The first television weather forecast was broadcast at 1pm on 3 November 1936 from Alexandra Palace, though this simply showed a map accompanied by a voice-over from an unseen broadcaster – not a weather expert. As with many such public services, televised forecasts were suspended during the war – all weather maps were considered secret documents – and were not resumed until July 1949. The resumption was prefaced by a talk by the wartime meteorologist, Dr James Stagg, whose forecasts were used when the D-day landings were planned and executed in 1944. But the format remained that of the pre-war broadcasts until the mid-1950s when forecasters appeared on screen for the first time to describe the maps. In those days the forecasters would carry the maps from the London Weather Centre and travel on the underground to the television studio before doing

Television weather broadcast, 1300 GMT 11 November 1936.
Crown copyright

WEATHER CHART FOR 1p.m. 11ᵀᴴ NOV. 1936

47

46

46

46

47

45

46

BBC television weather forecaster Geoffrey Leaf.
BBC

the broadcast! The system gradually became more elaborate, but the main map shown to viewers remained a hand-drawn chart on a perspex background showing the isobars and weather fronts.

Eventually a symbol chart was introduced using internationally agreed weather symbols. These are still used by meteorologists all over the world to explain the hundred or more different types of weather, but unfortunately they took a great deal of explaining. Most certainly they did not describe, to the viewer, the way that the weather would look. Indeed, you really had to understand the symbols before you knew what the weather was likely to be. In 1975 a BBC designer created the symbols that we use today and which have helped to explain weather broadcasts and make them more interesting.

There was still a problem with lack of visual movement in the forecasts and in the 1980s experiments were carried out using an electronic version of the weather charts.

This led to the present multi-changing system which is still unique in using a combination of what is called 'colour separation overlay' (CSO) and back projection.

In the weather studio a blank screen against which the forecasts appear is flooded with blue light from a back projector. Although the moving weather charts we see on our televisions look as if they are being displayed on the screen, this is not actually the case. The sequence of moving weather charts are electronically programmed to be fed directly into the studio

Post-1985 BBC television weather presentation with Michael Fish.
BBC

camera from a computer. The camera pointing at the screen is sensitive to the colour blue and when it picks up the blue light on the screen it is programmed to show the viewer the image of the moving weather map.

While viewers are able to see the changing maps, back in the studio the screen remains simply covered in blue light; the presenters do not see the same picture as the viewers. Two systems are used to overcome any problems that might arise from this. Firstly, the picture seen by viewers is relayed back to the presenters by means of an autocue positioned close to the camera they look at, so they can see the picture as it is broadcast. In addition, a very faint picture of the weather map is projected onto the blue screen which is visible to the presenters, but not to the viewers. This makes it easier for presenters to co-ordinate the weather charts they are describing with the picture the viewers are watching.

This may seem a complicated way of showing what will happen to the weather, but it gives a much clearer and more flexible picture than simply pointing a camera at a presenter standing in front of a weather chart.

However, there is one major snag! Presenters cannot wear blue clothes. If they did, as far as the viewers would be concerned, the presenters would disappear into the weather map like the blue screen behind. Data from the computers at Bracknell is sent down a telephone line to the television centre twice a day, with satellite pictures arriving every three hours. This information, made up of forecast weather maps of pressure, cloud cover and rainfall, is processed by the BBC graphics computers which draw the maps ready for broadcasting. (I should add that the Meteorological Office has set up a department dealing with weather forecasts for commercial broadcasting, including the well-known ITN weather forecasts. These differ from those of the BBC in that a mixture of meteorologists and lay presenters are used. When the broadcast is made by a lay presenter the script is written by a trained meteorologist at the Met Office.)

In addition, maps of weather conditions over Britain and the rest of Europe are constantly arriving in their office on fax machines. These are assessed by the forecasters who, after consulting with Bracknell and the London Weather Centre, decide on how to describe the forecast. British Isles symbol charts are constructed and these maps are placed in the order they have to be shown in the broadcast. A similar graphics computer in the television studio controls the sequence and speed of maps, so that when the forecaster presses a button the computer moves the appropriate map onto your screen.

A Day in my Life at the Television Centre

The weather is constantly changing and so therefore is the weather forecaster's day. But this is my typical working day

5.30: Alarm goes off.

6.00: Drive to west London to BBC.

6.30: Arrive at TV centre and collect keys from reception and go upstairs to weather centre. Log on three terminals, switch on rainfall radar and make some coffee. Accept the Bracknell forecast data which has arrived and been held awaiting instructions overnight. Check facsimile machine showing weather data over the British Isles and Europe and have a cursory glance at the prevailing weather patterns. Instruct the computer to draw up relevant weather maps from Bracknell. Have a more detailed look at the weather situation. Check *Radio Times* and Ceefax for broadcast times and also the office file for any weather-sensitive activities here and abroad (eg cricket test) and for any other interesting events and anniversaries.

7.30: Conference with the senior forecaster at Bracknell and London Weather Centre to discuss the weather trends for the day.

7.40: Decide on how to approach the various broadcasts of the morning shift according to their varying lengths. Decide on what is the story of the day – is it strong winds? If so how strong – could they do damage? Is the rain turning to snow? Will any rain cause or add to flooding? Will it be hot or cold? Also consider question of whether the weather is going to change – is a big change coming over next two to four days? And how confident are we of any change occurring?

7.50: Look at maps forecasting pressure, temperature, rainfall and clouds, sent from Bracknell and drawn up by computer on my instructions an hour ago.

8.00: Start drawing up symbols maps for the first British Isles forecast which is a detailed forecast for the southern region. Is it going to rain in Margate and not in Brighton? Is it going to be colder to the north of London than in Sussex? Look at the local radar rainfall maps and see where the rain is now and how it has moved over the last few hours. This broadcast is not just a potted version of the national broadcast but a genuine attempt at giving detailed advice for an area – albeit in a very brief broadcast. Draw maps for the 9am national broadcast which could be of as little as fifteen seconds duration.

8.30: Engineers arrive to switch on camera (the office doubles up as studio for all daytime broadcasts – the famous weatherman's window is seen behind us when broadcasting). Sit on studio chair to check lights and talk back to network director.

8.40: Place drawn electronic maps in order to be shown in the bulletin and copy them onto slide file.

8.45: Switch on lights, put in earpiece by which the network director communicates during the broadcast. Get dressed and ready for the broadcast. Make sure the countdown clock is working. (We work on a system whereby a digital clock appears on the camera lens counting the seconds down.) Practice broadcast.

8.56.50: South-east broadcast starts – clock counts down.

8.59.20: Cue to me to do the broadcast – has to finish exactly at 8.59.50 to link back to national news at 9am.

9.00: National news followed by first broadcast for the British Isles, lasting just fifteen seconds.

9.04: Switch off lights and prepare maps for 10am broadcast which is for the British Isles also and lasts one minute fifteen seconds. When completed put into bulletin and copy onto slide

In the television studio in 1987.
Crown copyright

file. Then concentrate on the weather over Europe and start to draw up the map for the 11am European bulletin.

9.50: Switch on lights, dress for camera, put in the earpiece and practice broadcast.

10.03: British Isles broadcast.

10.05: Continue drawing up the European maps. Decide approach to forecast remembering that you will be talking to British people who are possibly about to go on holiday. What are the skiing conditions like? Is it still windy in the Greek islands? Will the mistral blow again soon? Consider possibility of unsettled weather. Study reports from BBC travel unit; is it a public holiday, if so will roads be congested? All such questions have to be considered before putting the weather map into a bulletin to broadcast. When satisfied with the maps, put them into a bulletin and copy onto slide file.

11.03: European broadcast, two minutes thirty seconds.

11.30: Conference with Bracknell and London Weather Centre to decide on the weather over the British Isles for the next few days. If a Wednesday, have a further conference with the medium-range forecaster at Bracknell to discuss weather trends over the weekend and into the following week.

11.45: Check maps for British Isles broadcast at 12.03, put into bulletin and slide file.

12.03: British Isles broadcast, one minute fifteen seconds. Remember to say good *afternoon* . . .

12.05: Draw maps and prepare for main broadcast at 13.30. Look at maps for the south-east covering today, tonight and tomorrow. Put these together into a bulletin and slide file Draw Ceefax maps for today and tonight.

12.59: South-east broadcast, thirty seconds.

13.00: Switch slide file from office studio to presentation studio A.

13.10: Switch on computer system in presentation studio and rehearse broadcast. Place maps into presention slide file.

13.30: British Isles broadcast lasts two minutes thirty seconds (three minutes on Wednesday), standing up in front of camera.

13.40: Back to office studio, prepare for 14.00 broadcast.

13.50: Afternoon and evening shift presenters arrive.

14.01: Fifteen-second broadcast for British Isles on BBC 2.

14.05: Brief the afternoon staff on the British Isles weather; brief evening shift on European weather. Both shifts are at the same time, 14.00 to 22.30 – the afternoon shift concentrates on the British Isles weather and the evening shift on the European weather. The evening shift broadcasts to Europe on Super Channel, talking to Europeans in English, so must not use unfamiliar words, must not speak too fast and must remember to pause longer than usual at the end of sentences. The evening shift also broadcasts to the troops and their families in Germany going into great detail on their local weather.

14.30: Settle down in office for an hour or so for administration, deciding on roster for next few months or who will attend the exhibitions on behalf of the Met Office, or BBC. Or answer some of the scores of letters from viewers.

Also possibly have a meeting with the BBC producer to consider changes in graphics, new ways to produce bulletin, or perhaps a meeting with the computer system analysts to discuss a new product such as wind chill or comfort index.

16.30: Drive home – through London traffic!

18.30: Watch evening weather forecast before going out, perhaps, to a meeting or talk on changing weather patterns or TV weather broadcasts.

Ends.

The Meteorological Office

It is impossible to write a book about weather from a British perspective without dwelling at some length on the work of the Meteorological Office. The Met Office is not simply concerned with all the weather forecasts we see and hear in this country; it provides invaluable forecasting services for all branches of industry, agriculture, aviation, the armed forces, and is at the forefront of international attempts to form a global view of climate and climatic change. (A scientific team has been established at the Met Office to assess and study the likely nature and resulting impact of any such climatic changes.)

From its current headquarters, at Bracknell in Berkshire, the Met Office is in a unique position to monitor the world's weather at the centre of a vast international network of information gathering and exchange. Indeed what we see in the form of weather forecasts on the television and in our newspapers is no more than the tip of a very large iceberg. Overall the Met Office employs more than 2,300 staff and has a gross budget of some £100 million, of which around £40 million is recovered by charging for meteorological services. As the state meteorological service it is part of the Ministry of Defence though in a recent reorganization it has acquired executive agency status while still retaining its links with the MOD.

History

The Met Office traces it history back to 1854 when it was known as the Meteorological Department attached to the Board of Trade. Its first head was Admiral Robert FitzRoy, the captain of HMS *Beagle*, the ship upon which Charles Darwin sailed when he formulated his theories on evolution, which led to his most famous work *The Origin of Species*, published in 1859. The setting up of the new department was in part prompted by a naval catastrophe two years before when the British fleet was badly hit by a storm at Balaclava during the Crimean War. The concern, naturally, was that if this storm could have been predicted the losses it caused could have been prevented or significantly reduced. Up to this point there had been very little of what is known as 'synoptic meteorology', that is the preparation of all-weather charts based on the observation of prevailing weather conditions which could then be used to predict – or forecast – the weather.

Vice-Admiral Robert FitzRoy.
Crown copyright

The first daily weather report, September 3, 1860.
Trustees of the Science Museum.

	Sept. 3rd WEATHER REPORT. 1860. At 9 A.M.						
	B.	E.	M.	D.	F.	C.	I.
Aberdeen							
Greenock	30·07	55	52	WSW	2	1	b
Berwick							
Copenhagen							
Portrush							
(							
Hull	30·06	54	52	W	2	b	o
Liverpool							
Queenstown							
Helder							
Yarmouth	30·06	63	59	NW	2	5	c
London	30·13	50	54	W	2	2	b
Dunkirk	30·15	59	52	WSW	0	1	b
Dover							
Portsmouth	29·96	59	50	SW	3	3	bc

However, the development of telegraphy as a means of communication meant that the all-important observations needed for the preparation of up-to-date charts could be achieved. Under FitzRoy, who had learnt the value of keeping accurate records on the *Beagle*, the new department was able to prepare daily weather charts with the use of contemporaneous observations. They also received longer-term data from a host of other sources, including seamen and lighthouse keepers. Eventually, with the aid of telegraphed information from the rest of Europe the department began for the first time to prepare forecasts for three-day periods.

Unfortunately, after FitzRoy's death in 1865, this forecasting based on up-to-date observations – essentially the principle behind much of today's forecasting – was abandoned. The department itself was transferred from the auspices of the Board of Trade to the Royal Society.

The system then adopted was to base the forecast of storms – the supposed main function of the department – on the application of general rules of meteorology without reference to the crucial observations. The failure of this system saw the gradual return of FitzRoy's synoptic approach with daily

Readings being taken from a Stephenson screen.
Crown copyright

forecasts, as well as FitzRoy's use of the telegraph to warn coastal sites of impending storms.

The improvements of forecasting skills and an increase in the number of observations used, as well as the quality of instruments and techniques available to record data, saw the science of forecasting at the Met Office become more and more useful. Accurate records, which even now are of invaluable use to climatologists examining past weather records to determine possible future trends, became standard.

During both world wars the Met Office was of vital importance in forecasting weather conditions that enabled military planners to make decisions on the timing of assaults, not least for the D-Day landings of June 1944, where weather conditions played a crucial role. It is interesting to wonder whether the Spanish would have tried to invade England with the Armada in 1588 had they had access to reliable forecasting techniques! In the event, as I explain in another chapter, the fleet was cut to pieces both by the English navy and the severe storms.

After the Second World War the Met Office, in common with similar agencies around the world, began to take advantage of the advent of the computer age. The forecasting system devised

A Bristol fighter aircraft, dating from around 1926, modified for meteorological reconnaissance.
Crown copyright

by L.F. Richardson was essentially sound, but it had one minor snag. With mathematicians working out all the equations based on a given set of data the forecast would be hopelessly out of date – it was estimated that 64,000 mathematicians working day and night for a year could produce the forecast for just one day! However, the arrival of the computer age meant that such numerical weather prediction (NWP) became a practical possibility. The subsequent development in meteorology has concerned itself in part with producing more and more efficient computers in order to come up with more accurate and detailed forecasts. It was in 1965 that Bracknell first used numerical forecasts on a working basis, when the computer technology was finally good enough to produce sufficiently swift results. The use of technology, including the development of satellites, has become more important in enhancing our global picture of the world's weather. Also in 1972 and 1982 new and even more sophisticated numerical models of the atmosphere were adopted and programmed into the forecasting computer to increase the accuracy of the predictions. As we shall now see, the success of the Met Office, one of the most highly respected in the world, has made the NWP an indispensable part of British life.

The Met Office and its Work

As I said earlier, the Met Office is under the responsibility of the Ministry of Defence and the Chief Executive is ultimately responsible to the Secretary of State for Defence of the government of the day.

The aim of the Meteorological Office Executive Agency is to provide for United Kingdom military and civil users an effective, modern and efficient national meteorological service. In fulfilling its aim, the principal objectives of the Meteorological Office are to:

Provide a range of meteorological services to meet the requirements specified by the British armed forces and the Ministry of Defence Procurement Executive and approved by the Secretary of State for Defence.

• Provide under contract meteorological services to the Civil Aviation Authority.

• Make available warnings, forecasts and other meteorological services to shipping, the general public and others as may be required by the Secretary of State for Defence.

• Offer and provide on payment meteorological services to other government departments, commerce and industry.

• Provide information and advice to ministers as required by them on matters related to meteorology.

• Represent and maintain British interests within the World Meteorological Organization and other relevant international bodies.

• Maintain an up-to-date national meteorological library and national meteorological archive.

In meeting these objectives the Meteorological Office will:

• Aim to achieve progressively more demanding quality of service and efficiency targets.

• Pursue research to attain those levels of capability and expertise necessary to meet its objectives economically and on repayment to meet customer requirements.

• Develop and pursue profitable commercial outlets for its services within departmental guidelines.

• Maintain and renew the buildings and equipment needed for its operation in the light of forward plans agreed with the Ministry of Defence.

• Ensure that it recruits, trains and retains the right level and mix of personnel to meet its objectives in accordance with good employer practices.

Observing the Weather

Interconnection with the rest of the world is fundamental to the work of any weather forecasting body. The weather of the world is not isolated in pockets around the globe but forms one complete and ever-changing entity. This calls for constant and reliable information from all around the planet and the constant exchange of weather data between the forecasting agencies of the world is a major feature of these organizations.

People from every country regularly observe and record the weather and these observations are sent out in a uniform, common mathematical code which is recognizable to forecasters all over the world. In Britain these observations are received several times a day by the large computers at Bracknell. Such observations arrive from a variety of sources, not just from staff stationed at weather stations but increasingly from automated weather stations as well. There are around fifty of these in Britain supplying regular information to the Met Office and they are known in the jargon as SAWSs – synoptic automatic weather stations. Around the globe such stations are of obvious value in the more remote and inhospitable regions.

Herriot-Watt weather station, Cairngorms.
Kelly.

In the British Isles there is a network of some thirty 'key' observing stations with a distance of no more than 150 kilometres (94 miles) between any two. To supplement this there are the SAWSs plus another fifty-three stations manned by the Met Office to provide necessary detailed information. A semi-automatic station is now being developed for use at manned stations to release staff from some of the chores of observation, freeing them for other tasks.

However, the observations do not end there. There are auxiliary observers, people like coastguards, lighthouse keepers and private individuals, operating from some 124 sites and passing on additional information to the Met Office. Such people are invaluable and the Met Office works hard to recruit and assist them in their work.

Away from our shores, it is essential that data is obtained from the surface of the sea as frequently as possible. In the past this was chiefly gathered by full-time weather ships but increasingly the data comes from merchant shipping – anything from large oil tankers to banana boats! There are some 520 ships and oil rigs in what is known as the United Kingdom Voluntary Observing Fleet, which in turn is part of a huge World Meteorological Organization fleet which contains more than 7,000 vessels from nearly fifty countries. These ships telex or radio the information they gather to meteorological offices around the world via coastal radio stations. A new system, known as the Meteorological Observing System for Ships, is being introduced to make it easier for ships to send their data by satellite, thus ensuring a more accurate and faster transmission. Around the coasts of the British Isles, the Met Office is developing a network of nine 'key' offshore stations on oil rigs and light vessels. It should be remembered that while automation is a very effective way of making detailed observations, there is no single method which is capable of detecting all the required information. While machines can easily measure temperature or pressure, it still needs the judgement of the human observer to assess the type of cloud cover or type of precipitation.

So far we have only dealt with weather observations in two dimensions. It is equally important for forecasters to know what is occurring vertically in the atmosphere as well and there are various ways of doing this. One obvious technique that springs to mind is the use of satellites. The information that we receive from these is varied and, like other forms of data, interchangeable throughout the world. Since the first one went into orbit in October 1957, weather satellites have provided a dramatic leap forward in our ability to observe the weather systems by giving very high quality pictures. In addition, the use of infra-red cameras means that satellites are not restricted by lack of daylight and scanning can continue throughout the hours of darkness. Forecasters use satellite pictures to identify different sorts of clouds which in turn enable them to forecast how the clouds and associated weather will develop. They can be of particular help in assisting forecasters to pick out localized thunderstorms and areas of fog. Not only will they give a picture of clouds, but the images also show the temperature changes right down through the atmosphere to sea level, and even give an indication of the wind speed and direction shown by the movement of the clouds. All this extremely useful information is fed into the weather computer and helps to build up the very complex picture of the world's weather from which forecasters work. Satellites are of course extremely expensive and it is this area which once more shows the value of international co-operation in meteorology. Groups of nations team up to share the cost of launching satellites which can then provide data of value to all.

There are two types of weather satellite: the geo-stationary satellite and the polar-orbiting satellite. The geo-stationary satellite is placed around 36,000 kilometres (22,500 miles) above the Earth's surface and remains in a fixed position in relation to the ground below as the planet revolves. This type of satellite gives a picture of the clouds over a wide area. If there were five such geo-stationary satellites put up at regular intervals around the equator they would give a virtually complete picture of the clouds below every half hour. The computer-enhanced global picture they take can be made into a form of 'movie'. It is pictures from the European geo-stationary satellite Meteosat which we mostly see on our TV weather bulletins. Meteosat was built by the European Space Agency, of which Britain is a part, and is operated on behalf of the European National Weather Services. It provides most of the satellite data which is of direct interest to the Met Office.

The second type of weather satellites are the polar-orbiting satellites of which there are a considerable number. Most of the data relating to the British Isles that comes from this type of satellite is from those operated by the United States. Such satellites, at around 800 kilometres (500 miles), are much lower than the geo-stationary kind and orbit the earth once every 100 minutes, sending back pictures of cloud formations to ground stations as they fly through space. Because they are much lower, polar-orbiting satellites do not give a picture of such a large area as their geo-stationary cousin, but the pictures they do take have much greater detail, and with the benefit of enlarged high-definition pictures one can even make out the extent of snow cover at a particular spot, or the amount of sea ice. However, the pictures the polar-orbiting satellites provide are no good for running together as a sequence. As they orbit, the earth revolves beneath them so each pass is of a different segment of the globe and appears to be 28° further west each time – something in the order of 1,500 kilometres (940 miles).

As with other forms of weather observation, the use of satellite technology is constantly being updated. Over the next ten years more sources of information will come on stream, especially the new Meteosat Second Generation (MSG). This is intended to provide high-resolution imagery to provide even more detail. Similarly, the new generation of American polar-orbiting satellites is being upgraded. Even further ahead the Met Office is involved in a joint venture called the Earth Observing System between the European Space Agency, NASA, and the Japanese – a long-term project to launch polar-orbiting satellites to study the Earth's atmosphere and oceans in detail.

Releasing a weather balloon at the Campbell Island Meteorological Station.
Kim Westerkov/Oxford Scientific Films.

Apart from satellites there are other techniques used to gather upper–air and atmospheric data to complete the three-dimensional picture of the weather. One important source is weather reports from aircraft in flight which can give the meteorologist exact details of winds and temperatures, particularly in areas where there would otherwise be gaps in a forecaster's data. Nowadays this gathering is becoming automated and the information is fed to receiving stations via a geo-stationary satellite. As with ships, then, we can see that aircraft are involved in a two-way process with meteorologists; they provide some of the data to help draw up accurate forecasts, which, in turn, are used by the aircraft to help plot its course and avoid potential bad weather.

A very simple but still very effective and widely used technique for gleaning weather facts from the upper atmosphere is by sending up a balloon with a package of meteorological instruments, known as radiosondes, on the end. In Britain, as part of the global network of information gathering and exchange, these soundings are sent up twice a day from eight different stations around the country. The package is attached to a helium-filled balloon and tracked by radar – which enables us to calculate the wind speed and direction as the balloon ascends. The balloons normally reach a height of around 25 kilometres (80,000 feet) before bursting, when the package returns to Earth on a parachute. Most of the radiosondes disappear in the oceans but occasionally they are found on land. The packages contain instructions on how to return them in exchange for a small reward! The Met Office's radiosonde network has recently been modernized.

In recent years, radar has been used to 'tune' in to raindrops or snowflakes. This technique can not only show where it is

Aerial system of Decca type 42 weather radar.
Crown copyright

raining but also how heavily it is falling. To achieve this the Met Office has, in conjunction with other interested bodies such as local councils and water boards, developed a radar network which will eventually cover the whole of the British Isles. These colourful radar pictures, shown on our TV screens during forecasts, indicate the extent and heaviness of rain or snow by the use of different colours. This network is also linked to a similar system operating over continental Europe and can combine rainfall and cloud cover to give a picture to the forecaster of just where the thick rain-bearing cloud is. These radar images, combining several radars linked together, produce pictures every fifteen minutes and enable the forecaster to assess the likely movement and development of heavy rain and thunderstorms. All this information is also fed into the large weather-forecasting computers to give as accurate a picture as possible of the immediate weather conditions before any forecast is attempted.

There is another key element in data collection – communication. There is no point in assembling a comprehensive set of information about prevailing conditions if it is not collated and used quickly before it goes out of date. Bracknell stands at the centre of a huge worldwide communications network. It is constantly receiving (and passing on) data, screening it for accuracy, before swiftly feeding it into the mainframe forecasting computers for use.

How the Data is Processed

At the heart of the Meteorological Office's computer complex at Bracknell is a Cyber 205 which is capable of crunching numbers at a rate of 400 million every second! This computer is attached to an IBM 3081 and an IBM 3084 which are capable of performing the wide range of complicated work increasingly necessary. After receiving the worldwide data, the computers, using the quite simple mathematical equations which correlate to the basic physical laws of the atmosphere, produce a series of maps showing what the state of the atmosphere is like at the moment. By checking this against the computer forecast of what the atmosphere should be like, any large errors can be spotted and corrected. A team of expert forecasters working around the clock check to see if the computer has drawn up the weather maps correctly from the received data before allowing it to proceed to the forecast. If certain areas of the weather map are incorrect, perhaps showing that a hurricane has been placed slightly in the wrong place in the Caribbean, or that the winds circulating around it were not shown to be strong enough, then this team of forecasters actually invents weather observations and feeds them into it. This may seem odd, but this then helps the computer to draw the charts up correctly.

The computer system then starts the forecast procedure which it does twice a day using the data centred around the midnight and midday observations. Then, in a series of short time lapses, the computer uses its forecasting model to predict step by step how the atmosphere and hence the weather will change over the next week, producing weather charts to describe this. The computers are then used as a communications system to distribute the forecast weather maps to the forecasters. Some of this computer output is sent down telephone lines to other users. At the BBC it goes down into the computer graphic workshop where it is redrawn to give decent TV pictures that are used by the forecasters to tell the weather story on your screens.

The Clients

1 Defence

One of the primary functions of the Met Office is to provide weather information to the Royal Air Force, the Army and, in certain cases, the Royal Navy. Indeed, some 25 per cent of the Met Office's manpower is directed towards defence purposes. Until recently the majority of weather forecasters spent most of their time forecasting the weather for the Royal Air Force operations both at home and overseas. During the Falklands War a mobile unit of the Met Office accompanied the seaborne forces to Ascension Island and the Falklands, where they remain today in a civilian capacity. The forecasters receive the weather charts for the southern hemisphere from the computers at Bracknell and use them to forecast such things as local weather conditions for intricate military manoeuvres or for forecasting suitable clear skies with little turbulence to enable refuelling from tanker aircraft over the South Atlantic. Met staff are in fact based at several overseas service stations, most of them at operational RAF bases where their role is to monitor local conditions and brief crews as required. One of the most testing tasks is the forecasting for low-level flying of jet aircraft over Britain and over continental Europe for military exercise. Met staff also instruct service personnel in the basics of meteorology for aviation.

2 Civil Aviation

Civil aviation is the single biggest recipient of Met Office information and has a wide range of weather forecasting requirements. From supersonic commercial passenger flights to hang gliding, aviators rely heavily on weather forecasts. The forecasters, many of whom are still based at larger airports, are there to serve the needs of the Civil Aviation Authority.

The forecasters receive the data in the same way from Bracknell as any other, but use it in a different way. Because they are considering the needs of aircraft the forecaster is concerned about the strength of the winds in the upper atmosphere (which can blow up to 320km/h (200mph) or even 640km/h (400mph) at heights of 9,000 metres (30,000 feet). The strength of the winds will determine how much fuel an aeroplane will have to carry. The forecaster will also look to determine where areas of turbulence may occur for the aircraft to avoid and to monitor conditions around airports to see if they are safe for landings and take-offs. Thus the forecaster, in supplying the information to the air industry, has to bear in mind the twin concerns of safety and financial viability. A number of major airlines take data from Bracknell directly into their computers to assist them in their flight planning.

Aircrew using an aviation chart.
Crown copyright

The private flier is catered for by forecasts and weather information supplied by the Met Office through a service as defined by the Civil Aviation Authority. Training is available for such diverse activities as gliding, crop spraying or route flying by aircraft of private firms. Quite a lot of information for the private pilot is now available on the British Telecom's Prestel system for which the Met Office provides detailed flight forecast information.

Other Services

In recent years the Met Office has come under increasing pressure to become more commercially minded, as indicated by its new status as an executive agency. To that end, the selling of weather forecasts for specific operations as well as selling past data for planning purposes has become big business – to the tune of some £35 million a year. Of this the TV, radio and press forecasts we see and hear are just the tip of an ever-growing commercial iceberg. The Met Office has developed a strategic marketing plan to advertise to potential customers the advantage of taking a tailor-made service. These services vary a great deal, including, for example, the building contractor who wishes to have statistics of the weather, anywhere in the world, to help with the tendering and planning of contracts. He might also want a forecast for perhaps five days ahead to enable him to deploy his staff and materials in the most efficient way.

Agriculture is one industry which is very sensitive to the weather and needs forecasts both in the short and medium term. The BBC farmer's weather broadcast on Sunday lunchtimes, with a midweek update, gives a good general background. However, farmers also need far more detailed and localized predictions to maximize their efficiency. A special telephone consultancy, available to any customer for a small fee, allows direct access to a forecaster day or night to discuss detailed forecasts. Information is also supplied to the Agricultural Advisory Services to enable them to make predictions on weather-oriented animal and plant diseases, and to advise on soil evaporation as well as such things as siting for buildings, heating requirements and irrigation plans.

One neglected area in the past was forecasting specifically for road temperatures and the likelihood of ice and other hazardous wintry conditions. The Met Office's Open Road scheme now provides local highway authorities with daily information on road temperatures and surface conditions. The scheme can provide substantial savings for councils on occasions when forecasters predict that roads will not freeze and consequently will not require costly salting or gritting.

A crucial area of forecasting is for offshore oil and gas installations, which is carried out by the Met Office, not just for the North Sea but also for installations off South America and in the South China Sea. Some forecasters work *in situ* on oil rigs, and can be invaluable in advising on weather conditions likely to prevail during sensitive or difficult operations. The unsurpassed data bank of past weather observations, coupled with forecasting expertise, enables the Met Office computers to give excellent operational weather advice to offshore managers, as well as static or semi-static offshore oil rigs. There is an increasing need for merchant shipping to have advice on weather conditions across not just the Atlantic but all the major oceans of the world.

A team of master mariner meteorologists has been set up for several years at Bracknell to advise shipping companies on the best possible routes for their ships. Not every cargo needs to be transported in the quickest time – for some, the main priority is to be steered away from storm areas. Based on the world's most advanced global weather forecasting system, the team of master marine meteorologists advise ship owners on pre-voyage route planning. They monitor the ship's progress and give around-the-clock consultancy. In addition they provide the shipping company with an independent opinion on the performance of a chartered vessel or information to support a legal claim.

Other areas where the Met Office has extended its commercial activities include legal and insurance industries, storm–tide warning services and storm warnings.

Sunset over a drilling-rig on the Sleipner field in the North Sea.
Harry Nor-Hansen/Science Photo Library

The Met Office headquarters, Bracknell.
Crown copyright

How to Read and Understand the Weather Chart

The ability to be able to read and forecast the weather has long been one of man's most coveted dreams and there is no reason why the average person in the street should not be able to do some amateur forecasting of their own. With a mixture of observation, basic scientific knowledge and the help of TV or newspaper weather charts anyone can gain an understanding of the weather and start to predict some basic weather patterns. Of course, there is no guarantee you will get it right – even the experts get it wrong sometimes – but as well as increasing your knowledge you can have lot of fun with a spot of DIY forecasting.

I will start with the small amount of physics required, before moving onto the weather charts themselves and how they describe what is going on. There is no need to be daunted by the physical processes involved; most are observed in the everyday world surrounding us.

The first point to remember is that warm air rises – a fact we are aware of from simply observing hot-air balloons or from heating our homes. The next point to remember is that warm air can hold more water vapour before it becomes saturated, than can cold air.

When air rises above the ground it gradually enters a thinner atmosphere and expands. To enable it to expand in this way it needs energy which it draws from its own particles – which in turn causes the air to cool down.

As the air cools its ability to hold water vapour decreases; at 20°C (68°F) it can hold 15 grams per kilogram of dry air. At 10°C (50°F), this figure has dropped to 7.5 grams and by the time it has cooled to -10°C (14°F) it can only carry 1.5 grams per kilogram of air. If there is sufficient vapour present and the temperature drops enough, this vapour will begin to condense into tiny droplets, forming clouds. Rain can then occur by the smaller droplets colliding with each other until larger droplets are formed (called *coalescence*) and fall earthwards, but it is more likely that the air continues to rise and cool until the droplets form ice crystals. At this point a complex inter-reaction takes place within the cloud and larger crystals are formed which subsequently fall out of the cloud as snow, melting to form rain as they descend.

To make it more easily understood, the process of cloud formation can be seen as akin to a kettle boiling in a room. As the steam escapes it quickly condenses into water on cold surfaces.

We can see from this that whether we experience rain or not can depend on whether the approaching air (i.e. the wind) is rising, and also on how much moisture it contains. Clearly, if the air is very dry, even if it is rising into the colder upper atmosphere there would be insufficient water vapour to form clouds and create rain. An example of this would be a desert in the middle of a continent, where, although the air would be rising as a result of the heat, there would be no moisture to bring any rain.

So, when we consider the winds as they approach our shores we have to ask ourselves two basic questions. The first is: is the wind being *heated* from below or being *cooled down*? This will tell us if the air or wind will be rising or not. The second question is: has the wind been travelling over the land or the sea to reach us? From this the forecaster can determine if the wind is likely to have enough moisture within it to create cloud and rain.

Fig 1: North Atlantic analysis of 13 January 1977.
Crown copyright

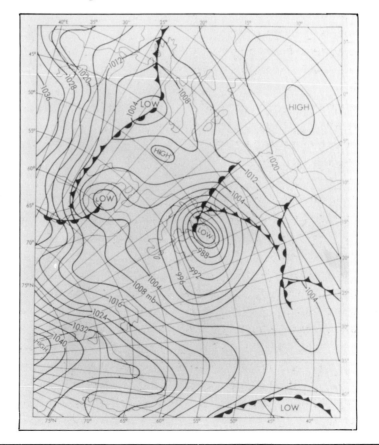

A quick look at a chart of the North Atlantic (Fig 1) shows that winds reaching the British Isles from the east and the south have come mostly over land, and will tend to be dry, while those from the north and west travel over water and will tend to have much more moisture – hence our wettest weather comes from those directions.

Armed with these basic observations we can now have a closer look at the weather chart, and explain some of the fundamental patterns we see on it.

Frontal Systems and Low-Pressure Zones

The chart above is a typical weather chart of the British Isles showing an area of low pressure indicated by the isobars packed tightly together.

To explain how we might arrive at such a situation, we need to travel westwards out into the Atlantic to consider what is happening there. As we can see in the diagram (Fig 2) our part of Europe lies in the path of chill winds from the Arctic which cross the North Atlantic onto our shores.

In the process the air is heated from below by the relatively warm seas, and also picks up moisture. Applying the principle outlined above we can see why this wind is often associated with wet, showery weather. It is known to forecasters as the polar maritime (Pm) air mass. However, another regular visitor is the air mass from the south-west known as the tropical maritime (Tm) (Fig 3). This hails from warmer climes and is thus cooled by the seas from which it also picks up considerable moisture. Now although the rules outlined at the beginning of the chapter would suggest that this air mass, where the air is not being heated from below and is not rising, would not tend to produce much cloud, simple experience tells us this is not the case. The south-westerly, our prevailing or most common wind, is in fact associated with coastal fog, low cloud and drizzle. The reason for this apparent anomaly is in the constant inter-reaction between the wind and the large waves in the Atlantic which results in the moist air circulating upwards, allowing cloud or fog to form as described earlier.

The situation becomes rather more complicated when two such air masses meet – this imaginary line where they meet is called a front. Most people have already heard forecasters use the terms *warm front* and *cold front* (Figs 4 and 5). Very simply a warm front is the boundary where a mass of warm air is

Fig 2: Direction of polar maritime airmass

Fig 3: Direction of tropical maritime airmass

Fig 4: Warm front

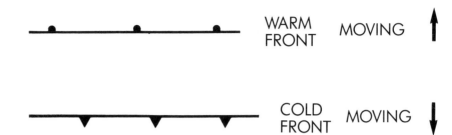

Fig 5: Cold front

displacing a mass of cold air, and is marked on charts with semi-circles on a line facing in the direction in which the warm front is heading. A cold front is where a mass of cold air is displacing warm air – and it is shown by triangles.

When these masses of cold and warm air meet out in the Atlantic, usually between 45° and 70°, it is known as a *polar front* (Fig 6) and it is from here that many of our typical low-pressure areas can develop.

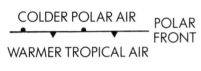

Fig 6: Polar front

Buckles begin to form along the straight polar front between the rival air masses, with the warm air displacing the cold in some places, and the cold pushing out the warm in others (Fig 7). Often this feature will produce no lasting effects. But at other times this process becomes more marked and air pressure begins to fall rapidly at the neutral point between the conflicting air masses, known as the *wave tip* (point A on Fig 7).

Fig 7: An embryo depression

When this occurs localized winds start circulating around this point – always in a anti-clockwise direction in the northern hemisphere – and the start of a low-pressure area is born (Fig 8). Note how you have an area of moist, warm air sandwiched between two areas of cold air; it is this feature that determines the weather we experience on the ground.

How Low Pressure Affects the Weather

As we have seen, if the pressure falls sufficiently at the wave tip we have the makings of a depression or low–pressure area. Exactly what makes the pressure drop at a given point more than another is determined by the upper atmosphere. Essentially the pressure drop is caused by more air 'escaping' from the imaginary column above the wave tip (*divergence*) than entering the column from below (*convergence*) (Fig 9).

Now the depression is formed, let us look at exactly how the weather we feel on the ground occurs. If we take a three-

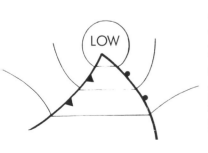

Fig 8: Beginning of a depression

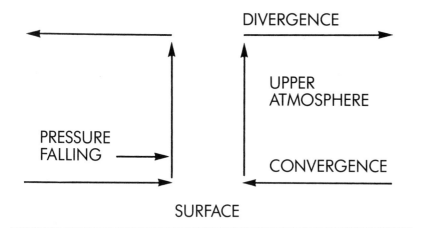

Fig 9: Simplified three dimensional wind pattern

dimensional look at the typical chart depression, we can see the 'sandwich' effect mentioned above more clearly (Fig 10). If we take the system to be moving from left to right on the page, an observer standing on the right would first experience cold air, then pass through the warm front, into what is known as the *warm sector*, through the cold front and back into more cold air. By this time our observer is likely to have experienced a considerable amount of rain.

The cloud and rain is formed according to the principles I outlined at the beginning of the chapter. We can see that as the warm front meets the cold air in front of it, the warmer less dense air mass gets pushed upwards. So we can see that as this warm, rising moist air approaches, clouds gradually begin to form which in turn lead to rain. At first the clouds forming will be very high, wispy cirrus clouds. Next come the thicker cirrostratus clouds giving the observer on the ground perhaps

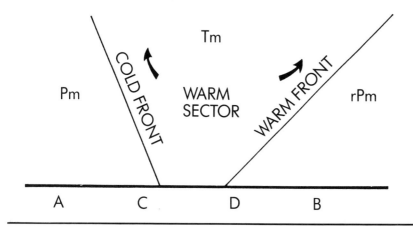

Fig 10: Three-dimensional section through the warm and cold fronts

the first clue that a change in the weather is on the way. It is these clouds that often produce a halo effect around the sun or the moon indicating the warm front's arrival.

As this diagram shows (Fig 11) the cloud becomes thicker and thicker over a period of some hours and over several hundred miles until rain falls on our observer, perhaps quite heavily, just as the warm front arrives.

After its arrival, however, the warm sector will typically produce low but not very thick cloud and though it will be overcast and possibly misty our observer should not experience anything more than drizzle. The next change occurs with the arrival of the cold front. As we can see, the warm air is pushed sharply upwards by the oncoming mass of denser cold air, creating thicker clouds and often heavy rain and blustery winds. This more violent ascent of the warm air is where thunderstorms can sometimes develop. The changeover associated with a cold front's arrival is often quicker than with a warm front, and soon the temperature drops as the colder air takes over and the weather becomes finer, though possibly with showers later on.

We have just seen two points on a low-pressure system where we can expect to find rain – the warm front and the cold front. The third is at the centre of low pressure itself. As already described, at this point there is a dispersal or divergence of air into the upper atmosphere, which means that the air is rising. If the ascent of air is fast enough, and assuming it has sufficient moisture, this process can lead to very heavy rain or even thunderstorms.

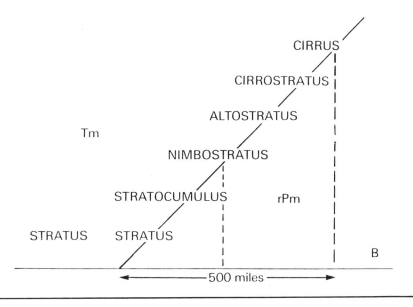

Fig 11: Cloud at a warm front

Occlusion

The pattern of the depression described above does not remain indefinitely. Cold air moves faster over the surface than warm air because of the latter's greater stability which increases friction with the Earth's surface. If we take a look at this in three dimensions, we will notice how the area of the warm sector touching the Earth's surface gets smaller and smaller as it is 'squeezed' upwards by the sandwich effect of the cold air, until eventually it is lifted up into the upper atmosphere altogether. This is known as *occlusion*.

Although our observer will still see the approach of the cirrus and other clouds as before, instead of experiencing the warmer, tropical maritime air he will find the air remains cool. On the weather chart this is shown by the line of the cold front moving much closer to the line of the warm front at the low-pressure point and eventually catching it up (Fig 12). This is often an early sign that the low-pressure system is starting to break up.

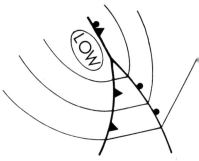

Fig 12: The occlusion process well under way

Winds

In this example of a depression moving across the British Isles the overall wind movement carrying the system across the country has been westerly, i.e. left to right. However, our observer on the ground will notice a variety of different wind directions, depending on where he is in relation to the centre of the low. A meteorological law, known as *Buys Ballot's Law*, states simply that if you stand with your back to the wind in the northern hemisphere, the area of low pressure is always to your left. By working backwards from the low, we can see that if our observer is standing on line A-B (Fig 13) with his left to the point

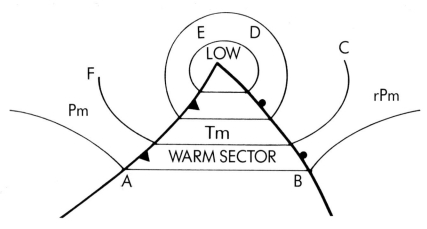

Fig 13: Wave depression.

of depression, then the wind at his back will be a westerly. On line B-C the wind will be southerly, on line D-E it will be easterly, while on line E-A it will be northerly. This explains the curious phenomenon we see sometimes of clouds moving in different directions. The clouds at the highest altitudes are being moved by the upper-atmosphere wind, while those at lower levels are propelled by more local winds associated with a depression. The strength of these local winds will be in proportion to the depth of the depression.

Pressure

One of the first signs a forecaster gets that a low may be forming out in the Atlantic, as described above, is by a rapid fall in pressure monitored by an observation ship. The rapidity of the fall will often give an idea of the likely strength of the wind, which on charts is shown by the closeness of the isobars.

As a frontal system approaches, an observer's own barometer can give a good indication of the stages it is at. As the denser cold air is replaced by the less dense warm air the pressure (which simply measures the 'weight' of air above a point) will naturally drop. Once the warm sector has arrived the pressure will stabilize. After the arrival of the cold front the pressure will rise again.

Anticyclones

These are areas of high pressure and are generally associated with fine, quiet weather – cold in winter, hot in summer. Unlike in low-pressure areas where the air is rising, allowing clouds to form, in anticyclones the air is falling. Having said this, stratocumulus cloud can sometimes form, especially if the anticyclone is near the sea, and this can cause those dry but gloomy days we experience in winter.

Mystery and History of Weather

Climate has had a profound effect on the way man lives. From the earliest times, the weather has dictated where man has made his home, the timing of his migrations and altered the course of battles and wars. Napoleon's march on Russia in 1812 was stopped in its tracks by an exceptionally severe Russian winter. Similarly, Hitler's invasion of the Soviet Union during the last war was hit hard by appallingly cold weather. In this chapter I will look at how the climate has affected the development of civilization, and also at how the importance of weather has become reflected in many sayings and items of folklore. But first I consider how weather conditions contributed to one of the greatest triumphs in England's history – the defeat of the Spanish Armada in 1588.

The Spanish Armada

In 1588 England was under threat of invasion by the Spanish. The two countries of different religions, Spain Catholic, England Protestant, had been at each other's throats for years and it seemed some conflict was inevitable. The Spanish were also angry about the way English sailors, notably Francis Drake, had been attacking and looting their ships laden with treasures from the New World, of which Spain claimed ownership.

There are many reasons why the Spanish fleet, the mighty Armada, failed in its plan to launch an invasion of southern England – the brilliance of the English sailors, including of course Drake; the knowledge they had of local currents and tides; and the inability of the Spanish ships to adapt to new naval fighting techniques. However, there is no doubt that the weather played its part in the defeat of the Armada, culminating in the terrible storms that destroyed many Spanish vessels as they fled for home around the north of the British Isles.

Using some of the weather observations carried out at the time, analysis of the prevailing weather conditions has been carried out by the climatic research unit at the University of East Anglia. Synoptic weather charts have been drawn up using the latest techniques of weather analysis. This sheds interesting light on the cause of the winds and bad weather which so disrupted the Armada, and also provides an intriguing insight into the weather of the British Isles during the period of the Little Ice Age.

The Weather Trend

King Philip of Spain, a thoughtful and deliberate monarch, could hardly have picked a worse year for the invasion. The summer of 1588 was wet and windy, at least in the Channel where the ships were bound, with a large number of storms. Indeed one wonders whether Philip, with the benefit of modern forecasting techniques, would ever have undertaken such a daunting mission had he known of the impending weather conditions. It seems that although the British Isles experienced twice as many anticyclonic weather days as cyclonic days in 1588, the reverse was true over the seas where the Armada sailed. It appears that there was a period of stagnatary weather, that is where the movement of weather systems was 'blocked', in this case by the presence of a high-pressure area or anticyclone to the north-west of the British Isles. This halted the movement of depressions or low-pressure areas northwards towards the North Pole. Another feature was that ocean currents from the north were seemingly rather stronger, and colder, than is common in this century. (Remember on average the Little Ice Age was considerably colder than now and, as mentioned in Chapter 1, during the 16th century the Thames froze over a number of times.) This may be the factor behind some of the fog that the Armada encountered, formed as warm air passes over a colder sea. Detailed analysis also indicated that the jet streams, the upper winds which are the 'driving force' of our weather systems, were at times considerably stronger during the summer than those of the present day. The strongest was in the order of 256km/h (160mph). Meanwhile the surface winds, that is the ones we notice down on the ground (or more importantly in this case at sea), reached up to 80km/h (50mph) or more, with gusts perhaps up to 120km/h (70mph) on occasions – certainly a hazardous proposition for the sailing ships of the time, as the Spanish were to find out.

The Approach of the Armada

The Armada fleet, totalling around some 120 ships, did not set sail until late July 1588. This followed an abortive attempt by the British fleet some time earlier to destroy the Spanish menace before it had even left harbour.

In the first few days of its voyage towards the English Channel, the mighty fleet experienced near-perfect sailing conditions to speed it on its way. As the fronts associated with a low-pressure

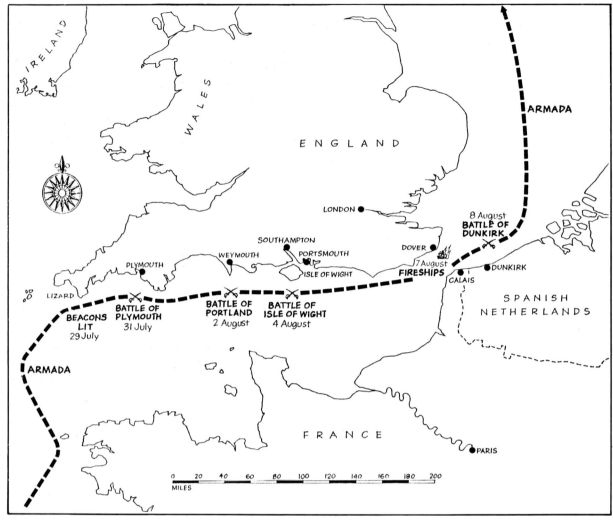

The passage of the Spanish Armada through the English Channel and the principal battles fought in the late summer of 1588.

area moved north-east across the Atlantic, strong south-westerly winds sprang up. The commander of the fleet, the duke of Medina Sidonia, had cause to write that 'no better weather could have been desired'. However, that apparent good omen was not to last. By 26 July conditions were very different; as the centre of a depression passed over, a thick fog developed, in which the fleet was becalmed, followed later in the day by squally winds and then heavy rain. The latter was probably caused by a cold front moving behind the depression.

Worse was to come, however. The next day the depression must have deepened and gale-force winds developed which caused early casualties in the fleet. The four galleys, which contained slaves chained inside to power the ships with oars, were unable to cope with the bad weather and were forced to turn back; one was later wrecked on the French coast. The duke reported that the waves 'reached to the skies' and that it was 'the most cruel night ever seen'.

It was on 29 July that the Armada spotted land, Lizard Point in Cornwall. At this time, the wind was still south-westerly which assisted the Spanish ships on their way. What worried the English was that part of their fleet was in Plymouth taking provision and that a strong south-westerly could trap them in the port, leaving the Spanish a free hand to travel down the Channel. (The Spanish plan was to link up with the duke of Parma further up the Channel and protect the crossing of troops in shallow invasion barges as they made their way to the English coast from Dunkirk and other invasion ports.)

However, the English were master sailors and this, coupled with a change in winds, meant that they were able to get out of port and engage the Armada on 31 July in the first battle of the campaign. Here the Spanish were fooled by a mixture of the English guile and the winds. For as they approached along the coast on 30 July the Armada saw the English ahead of them; this meant that the English were downwind, to the advantage of the advancing Spaniards. However, overnight the English managed to manoeuvre behind the Spanish, much to their astonishment, and the resulting skirmish led to a small but significant victory for the English ships. This took place in increasingly rough seas as the cold front of a depression arrived.

The next two battles, at Portland on 2 August, and off the Isle of Wight on 4 August, were both fought during a period of relatively settled weather. A high had moved in and dominated the weather picture for the next few days, with fairly light winds. The English sailors were on each occasion able to draw on knowledge of local conditions to their favour, using first the breezes coming off the land and then adapting to the south-westerly which sprang up regularly later in the day. Although the sailors of this time naturally lacked many of the navigational techniques we have now, they had a very good grasp of basic weather patterns, coupled with knowledge of tides and currents. This gave the English a tremendous advantage.

Both sea battles ended in victories for the English, although the Armada was still able to continue on its way up the Channel for its rendezvous. This did not displease the English, for the rest of their fleet was waiting there also; and for the first time they would have a numerical advantage over the Spanish.

The mainly calm weather continued until the weekend of

6 August, by which time a westerly wind had sprung up. The two opposing fleets had made their way quietly down towards Calais, both running low on ammunition. On the Saturday, the Spanish anchored off Calais, by which time the anticyclone was moving off over continental Europe and a new depression was tracking in across the British Isles.

It was at this time that the English perhaps exploited the weather conditions to their greatest advantage. The strategists on the English side appreciated that the wind was blowing from the south-west and west, and that on the night of Sunday 7 August, there would be a strong spring tide. Both wind and tide, then, would be running towards the Spanish fleet from the English position, an ideal situation in which to launch fireships in the middle of the night. This is precisely what they did. Eight ships were set ablaze and then directed towards the anchored Armada. The tactic caused pandemonium, with many of the Spanish ships not even pausing to haul up their anchors and instead cutting their mooring lines before floating off, some helplessly, into the night.

The duke recorded it like this:

'At midnight two fires were seen kindled in the English fleet which increased to eight; and suddenly eight ships with sail set, and fair wind and tide, were seen coming straight for my flagship and the rest of our fleet, all burning fiercely.'

Another eyewitness said:

'. . .the whole eight fireships went drifting between the fleet and the shore with the most terrible flames that may be imagined.'

The next day, 8 August, the Armada was in near total disarray. The elements, it seems, were almost entirely in favour of the English. The fresh south-west and north-westerly winds helped the English to bear down on the Spanish who were now in danger on two fronts. Firstly, from the guns of the English fleet itself off Dunkirk, and secondly, there was a growing fear for them that the Armada would be driven on to the sandbanks at Zeeland by the winds and tide.

In fierce fighting the Spanish lost a number of large ships and it was at this point, perhaps, that the Armada ceased to be a serious threat to England. At sunset, with a heavy sea running and winds blowing hard, one Spaniard wrote disconsolately:

'Hardly a man slept that night – we went along all wondering

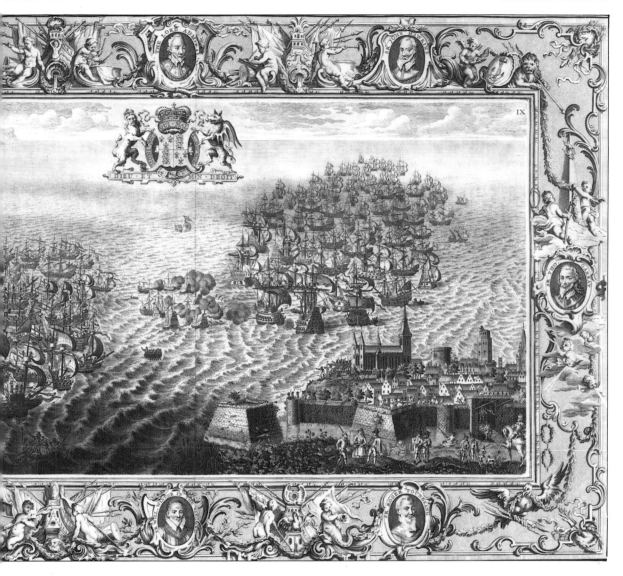

Launching the fire-ships against the Armada. From a line engraving by J. Pine after C. de Lempriere.
National Maritime Museum, Greenwich

when we should strike one of those banks.'

On 9 August, the position for the Spaniards looked no less bleak. The winds were still driving them towards the shore with the English navy sailing menacingly behind them. There was a danger that the entire fleet could be lost. The duke summed it up graphically:

'At daybreak the north-west wind fell somewhat and we discovered the English fleet of 109 ships rather over half a league astern. It was going to be impossible to save a single ship of the Armada as they must inevitably be driven by the wind onto the banks of Zeeland.'

However, it was at this point that the weather intervened crucially once more in the fate of the Armada, when a 'miraculous' change in the wind direction suddenly brought brief safety to the stricken fleet. What happened from a meteorological point of view was that the approach of a sharp ridge of high pressure from the west caused the wind to swing from a north-westerly to a south-westerly or west-south-westerly direction. This meant that the Spanish were blown out into the North Sea rather than onto the shore, and were thus given an escape route from the English fleet. For the Spanish this was clearly the hand of God at work. The duke wrote:

'God was pleased to change the wind to west-south-westerly, whereby the fleet stood towards the north without hurt to any ship . . . .'

Of course, the wind was not the only thing that saved the Spanish. The fact that the English fleet were desperately short of ammunition meant that, to their frustration, they were unable to follow up their advantage with a final crushing blow. In any case, for the Spanish it was rather like jumping out of the frying pan into the fire. Although they escaped the sandbanks and the marauding English as the strong south-westerlies carried them further out into the North Sea, the Spanish were only just beginning a confrontation with their biggest foe – storms. Unwilling to face the English navy again, and unaware of the latter's chronic shortage of ammunition, the Spanish Armada decided to head for home up through the North Sea, around the north of the British Isles and then back home to Spain via the North Atlantic. Unfortunately for them, with the autumn approaching they were bound to encounter poor weather passing through more northern latitudes. As one English sea captain sagely remarked:

'the season of the year considered, with the long course they have to run and their sundry distresses, and, of necessity, the spending of time by watering, winter will so come on as it will be to their great ruin.'

So it was to prove. On 15 August they experienced an early taste of the weather to come, with a ferocious storm which saw many of the pursuing English fleet put to port. This was caused by the arrival of a very vigorous low blowing in from the Atlantic.

But the real disaster for the remnants of the rapidly disintegrating Armada came on 21 September off the west coast of Ireland. A terrible storm, probably the remains of a tropical storm, sank at least seventeen of the Spanish vessels and badly damaged others.

So it proved that what the English had started, with their sailing and fighting skills, the weather had completed; that is, the total rout of the Armada. It would be going too far to say that the weather determined the course of the fate of the Spanish Armada; but there is no doubt that it intervened significantly at various crucial moments during the summer of 1588.

Weather chart showing the storm that struck on 21 September 1588 and effectively completed the destruction of the Spanish Armada.

K. S. Douglas, H.H. Lamb, C. Loader.

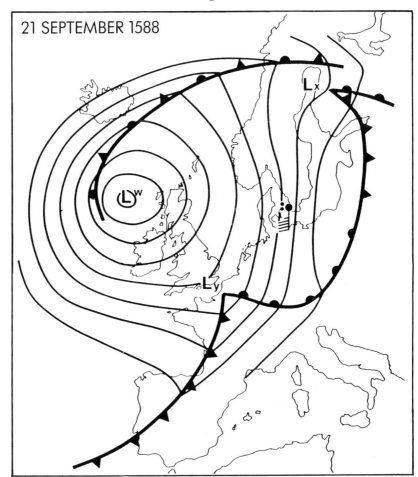

21 SEPTEMBER 1588

Other Battles

There have been numerous other battles in history where the weather has played an important, and sometimes crucial, part. The D-Day landings in 1944 was an occasion when the timing of the Allied invasion was linked closely with the weather predictions. Also in the Falklands conflict of 1982, forecasters from the Met Office travelled to the South Atlantic to give advice to the military commanders about local conditions. Indeed there is still a Met Office station there.

One of the most large-scale effects of the weather was in Hitler's invasion of the Soviet Union in the last war. Although there were many factors in his eventual defeat, the harshness of the Russian winter coming down on the embattled German troops undoubtedly played its part, similar to the demise of Napoleon's invasion in the previous century.

Climate and Civilization

Tens of thousands of years ago early man found himself living in an environment considerably different from that of today. The world was in the grip of the last Ice Age, when average temperatures were several degrees lower than today, when ice sheets and glaciers spread over parts of Europe that are now largely ice-free, and when the sea levels were much lower than those we now have. At such a time, our ancestors often lived in caves and it is from their drawings on walls that we get a first glimpse of early man's view of the world and the climate around him. For instance, in parts of what is now Russia there are cave drawings of mammoths, the hairy-coated elephants, and evidence that they were hunted by men.

Although the weather was certainly bleaker and harsher than now, there were compensations. The reduced sea levels meant that the land masses which now constitute the Soviet Union and the United States were joined, allowing man to migrate across in search of food or better climatic conditions. This probably accounts for the Asian traits in the appearance of the American Indians, whose ancestors probably roamed over from Asia, crossing a stretch of land which later became swamped by rising sea levels to become the Bering Straits. It was at this time too, some 40,000 years ago, that man probably first reached Australia, when sea levels were at their lowest and Asia was not far from the Australian mainland.

Although the climate was bad, the Ice Age did at least allow man to move around over land in search of new and better territories to inhabit. Once the end of the Ice Age came, life changed and, initially at least, colonies of people became more isolated. Gradually the sea levels began to rise, reclaiming many of the coastal areas where man had settled to take advantage of fishing possibilities. It is probably from this time that myths and legends of the Ancient World arose, such as the disaster of the lost city of Atlantis. Also many of the stories of catastrophic floods that appear in various mythologies and religions around the world may hark back to this time of fast-rising sea levels. Over hundreds and thousands of years the melting of the ice caused the sea to rise; even recent experience in the North Sea shows that such rising levels coupled with high spring tides and fierce onshore winds can bring freak and destructive floods.

By around 7,000 years ago, that is about 5000 BC, the Earth had shaken off the coldness of the Ice Age and indeed temperatures were on average higher than today. It was around this time that the rising sea levels achieved something which was to have a profound effect on the future of Britain – we became an island.

The low-lying lands between what are now Dover and Calais began to flood – probably removing a number of settlements – until it became swamped altogether. The history of the British Isles could then begin! Other parts of the world were affected by the fluctuating climate. The Sahara, now a symbol of dry barren aridity, seems to have been a much wetter and more fertile region some 5,000 to 6,000 years ago. Cave paintings show that giraffes, hippopotami and elephants lived there, all of which would find it impossible now. Man of course had to follow his food supply and as the Sahara turned increasingly to desert so man moved either south, or north, towards the still-fertile Nile region where the Egyptian civilization began to flourish.

In western Europe the warmer conditions that came in this post-glacial age saw the gradual beginnings of civilization, and with less stormy and extreme weather, sea travel from the warmer, more civilized areas to more northerly parts became more common. Also at this time the great forests of western and northern Europe spread, covering areas like Cornwall and the north-west Highlands of Scotland and even parts of Iceland. In the warmer climate man was also able to inhabit higher and more northerly areas of ground. A period of cooling, however, seems to have set in 4,000 to 5,000 years ago, bringing wetter weather to some parts of northern Europe but some drier weather to parts of Africa as the aridity and size of the deserts increased in the sub-tropics. This often caused the migration of peoples seeking more fertile areas and often sparked off wars as the migrating groups came into conflict with the existing

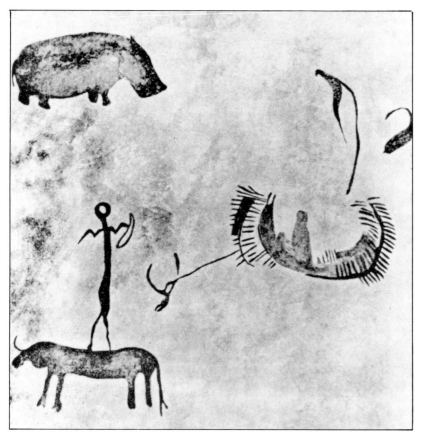

Cave painting from the Sahara indicating the wetter climate that once prevailed there.
Random Century Group

inhabitants of more desirable regions.

The last millennium BC, when this cooling period was still prevalent, saw the rise of the Greek and then the Roman civilizations. It would appear that the climate then in that part of southern Europe was wetter and hence more fertile than now. This was also the case with the extreme north of the African continent which saw the flourishing of the city of Carthage, in what is now Tunisia, as it grew to challenge the might of Rome. There were indeed times when the River Tiber, on the banks of which Rome was built, even froze over. The moister climate allowed cities to flourish, such as Petra, which is now buried in the arid rock and sand of the Jordanian desert. This period of history saw the growth of great learning and culture which were to influence western civilization for many hundreds of years, and still have a significant impact.

The climatic fluctuations continued, and in the first few hundred years AD there was a period of warming, followed by a period of cooling, around AD 300 onwards, which may have triggered off droughts in central Asia, causing the nomadic

The once flourishing city of Petra, now an arid waste.
Aerofilms Limited

tribes there to head west in search of more fertile regions. This was perhaps the start of the 'Barbarian' hordes who heralded the end of the great ancient civilizations and helped plunge Europe into the so-called Dark Ages.

The Norsemen were natural adventurers and headed westwards in their longboats. By AD 870, the Vikings had reached what we now call Iceland. Although there was certainly some ice there at the time, there is no doubt also that the climate of Iceland was warmer than today, and it rapidly became a Viking settlement and a springboard for explorations further west. By the late 980s, the Vikings had reached the land they called Greenland. Anyone visiting Greenland today would consider it a strange name to be given – it is one of the more inhospitable inhabited regions of the world. Certainly it is claimed that Greenland was given its name to 'persuade' other settlers to sail and settle there. But undoubtedly the warmer climate then made it a much more pleasant area to live than now.

Spurred on by their worship of Thor, the thunder god to whom the Vikings prayed when they ventured westwards, the Norsemen continued to brave the seas and push onwards. Their ability to establish a colony in Greenland was helped by a relative scarcity of stormy weather experienced in this period of warmer climate. The biggest discovery for the Vikings came around AD 1000 when, blown off course, Leif Eriksson landed on the east coast of America. The Vikings called the land Vinland or Wineland and it seems clear that settlements were established, with Greenland used as a staging post for Scandinavia and Iceland. But the Little Ice Age came and gradually the number of storms, and particularly icebergs and ice fields increased from around AD 1200 onwards. This effectively cut off the routes to America and eventually Greenland too was abandoned as a colony. The great era of Viking exploration had come to a chilly end.

As climate changes man always has to adapt to meet the new challenges. This is as true now as at the beginning of human civilization. The greenhouse effect and global warming, which are expected to bring rising sea levels and a changed pattern of rain distribution, are the new challenges for mankind. But unlike in the past, man has been able to predict to some extent the advent of these new problems and, unlike his ancestors, modern-day man is able to anticipate some of the correct responses.

The Folklore of Weather

Science has now gathered together a formidable array of technological tools to help in the process of forecasting the weather; satellites, radar, automatic weather ships to name but a few. And, despite the critics, we forecasters get it right more often than not.

In the past, however, man had no such technology nor had he

the scientific understanding of the processes of climate we have today. People did not have daily forecasts to guide their lives as today when newspapers, radio and television broadcasts are full of them. Do I put the washing out? Will the day be fine enough to make hay? Quite naturally, to answer these questions, people from early civilization right up to comparatively modern times have come up with their own methods of weather predictions. These have become the folklore of weather.

In some cases a few of the better home-spun pieces of wisdom are still used, especially by people such as farmers who, after all, know their local weather conditions better than anyone. By and large, however, they have become part of our language and culture but have ceased to have any practical application. While a few have some sound basis in fact, most are colourful but highly inaccurate or completely misleading!

One of the better ones, and significantly it has survived better than most, is the old saying, 'Red sky at night, shepherd's delight; Red sky at morning, shepherd's warning.' There is some basis for this. The sun sets in the west and, shining up to a cloud layer to give the distinctive and often beautiful glowing red colour, it can signify that a front, which produces rain, has passed. The reverse is the case with the sun rising in the east in the morning. However, it is still safer to rely on the BBC television forecast at 9.30pm – even for shepherds!

Another popular piece of folklore is the saying that if it rains on St Swithin's Day (15 July) it will rain for forty days; if it is fine it will remain fine for forty days. As a piece of folklore it is a very good part of our heritage. Unfortunately it has little or no meteorological standing. It is true that if there is a high-pressure area settling over the country by 15 July giving good weather, the chances are that it will remain for some time. But it would be a brave person who booked a holiday just on the evidence of the St Swithin's Day 'rule'!

Still, the folklore is fun and, as long as it is not taken too seriously, quite harmless. The British, with their traditionally changeable seasons and preoccupation with the weather, have spawned more than their fair share of folklore. Expressions about the weather are not merely forecasting; they contain all types of descriptions and observations, reflecting the deep importance weather has always played in our lives.

Here is a selection of weather folklore and sayings both from these shores and the rest of the world.

Weather Phenomena

'No weather is ill, if the wind be still.'

'Every wind has its weather.' – Francis Bacon.

'Cloudy mornings turn to clear evenings.'

'Clouds without wind in summer indicate wind.' – Theophrastus.

'If clouds be bright,
'Twill clear tonight;
If clouds be dark,
'Twill rain – do you hark?'

'If clouds look as if scratched by a hen,
Get ready to reef your topsails then.'

'Mackerel sky and mare's tails,
Make tall ships carry low sails.'

(Both these last two are old sayings used by sailors whose lives could sometimes depend on gauging the weather correctly; they were useful indicators to the approach of a warm front and a strengthening of the winds.)

'Trace in the sky the Painter's brush,
Then winds around you still will rush.'

'Dappled sky is not for long' – French saying.

'A blue and white sky,
Never four-and-twenty hour dry.'

'A bench of clouds in the west means rain.'

'The rain it raineth every day.' – Shakespeare.

'Much foam in a river foretells a storm.'

'A foot deep of rain,
Will kill hay and grain;
But three feet of snow
Will make them come more.' – Devon expression.

'Though it rains, do not neglect to water.' – Spanish expression.

'Rainbow to windward, foul falls the day;
Rainbow to leeward, damp runs away.'

'Philosophy will unweave a rainbow.' – Keats.

'A white frost never lasts more than three days.'

'Rain before seven, fine before eleven.'

'A hailstone by day denotes a frost at night.'

'Corn is as comfortable under the snow as an old man is under his fur coat.' –Old Russian saying.

'Quick thaw, long frost.' – Anglo-Saxon saying.

'If it rains on Sunday before Mass it will rain all week.'

'A fog from the sea brings honey to the bee;
A fog from the hills brings corn to the mills.'

'With dew before midnight,
The next day will sure be bright.'

'When the Lizard is clear,
Rain is near' – Cornish saying.

'Sunshiny rain,
Will soon go again.'

'Can any understand the spreadings of the clouds?' – Old Testament.

'White mist in winter indicates frost.'

'A good hearing day is a sign of wet.'

'When pigs carry straw to their sties, bad weather may be expected.'

'If old sheep turn their backs towards the wind, and remain so for some time, wet and windy weather is coming.'

'Pigeons wash before rain.'

'Turkeys perched on trees and refusing to descend indicate snow.'

'If pigeons return home slowly the weather will be wet.'

'Sharks go out to sea at the approach of a wave of cold weather.'

'When trout refuse bait or fly, there is ever a storm a-nigh.'

'If many earth worms appear, it presages rain.'

'If glow worms shine much, it will rain.'

'The louder the frog, the more the rain.'

'Fast runs the ant as the mercury rises.'

'If woodlice run about in great numbers, expect rain.'

'When the butterfly comes, comes also the summer.' – Saying of Zuni Indians.

'When a cat sneezes it is a sign of rain.'

Heavenly Bodies

'When the sun sets sadly, the morning will be angry.' – Zuni Indians.

'Evening red and morning grey,
Two sure signs of one fine day.'

'A bright circle around the sun denotes a storm and colder weather.'

'The circle of the moon never fills a pond; the circle of the sun wets a shepherd.'

'Pale moon doth rain,
Red moon doth blow,
White moon doth neither rain nor snow.' – Latin proverb.

'If a snowstorm begins when the moon is young, it will cease at moonrise.'

'When the stars begin to huddle,
The earth will soon become a puddle.'

'The sun sets weeping in the lowly west,
Witnessing storms to come, woe and unrest.' – Shakespeare, *Richard II.*

But perhaps the best of all sayings about the weather, one which puts much folklore in its place is this one:

'Was it always spring weather?
No, we were young and together.'

'The last Sunday in the month indicates the weather of the next month.'

Seasons

'Ice in November to bear a duck,
The rest of the winter'll be slush and muck.'

'Hoar frost on 1st May indicates a good harvest.'

'A cold May gives full barns and empty churchyards.'

'Dry August never brings dearth.' – Italian saying.

'A sharp April kills the pig

'April snow breeds grass.
Till April's dead,
Change not a thread.'

'The uncertain glory of an April day.' – Shakespeare.

'Thunder in spring, cold will bring.'

'Calm water in June, Sets corn in tune.'

'A shower of rain in July, when the corn begins to fill, is worth a plough of oxen, and all belongs theretill.'

'Warm October, cold February.'

'Dirty days hath September,
April June and November;
From January up to May,
The rain it raineth every day.
All the rest have thirty-one,
Without a blessed gleam of sun;
And if any of them had two-and-thirty,
They'd be just as wet and twice as dirty.'

'Ice in November, brings mud in December.'

'There are always nineteen fine days in October.' – Kent saying.

'Whitsunday wet, Christmas fat.'

'On Michaelmas Day the devil puts his foot on the blackberries.'

'Do not abuse the year until it has passed.' – Spanish saying.

'Spring has come when a maid can set her foot on seven daisies at once.'

'One swallow does not make a summer.'

'Much fog in autumn, much snow in winter.'

'A green winter makes a fat churchyard.'

'Summer in winter, and summer's flood,
Never boded an Englishman good.'

'If the ice will bear a goose before Christmas, it will not bear a duck afterwards.'

'A winter fog will freeze a dog.'

The Animal Kingdom

'If cocks crow during a downpour it will be fine before night.'

'If the birds be silent, expect thunder.'

'When woodpeckers are much heard, rain will follow.'

'If the cuckoo does not cease singing at midsummer, corn will be dear.'

'Petrels gathering under the stern of a ship indicates bad weather.'

'Cattle go to the hills before rain.'

'Cows lying down is a sure sign of rain.'

'If bulls lick their hoofs or kick about, expect much rain.'

Future Climate

We have all heard people talk nostalgically about how the summers always seemed longer and hotter in their youth; how the sun always shone, and 'rain stopped play' was almost unheard of at cricket matches. Just the tricks of memory we may think. But in fact there is some limited truth in this. If one examines the average temperature records for the whole globe, some interesting facts are revealed. The early part of the century, particularly the years 1910 to 1940, was indeed warmer than average and coincided with a great flowering of agricultural success in many parts of the world. After the war, there was a period of gradual cooling followed by warming in the 1970s and then the 1980s, the warmest decade of the century and one of the warmest since accurate records were kept. Indeed,1989 was the warmest year recorded since 1659.

In recent history the weather in Britain was much colder than now. Our view of the traditional white Christmas stems from early Victorian times when there was a series of snowy Christmases and very low temperatures. Among others, Charles Dickens drew on such experiences for many atmospheric scenes in his work, notably in *A Christmas Carol*. Nowadays, snow at Christmas in the southern half of the country is very rare indeed – and the bookmakers have not had to pay out on the annual white Christmas bets for many years! However, there is a crucial lesson to be learnt here. With everyone nowadays rightly concerned about changes in climate we should remember that man is very adaptable to change and, as the saying has it, life goes on. Indeed, the chilly centuries of the Little Ice Age also produced the likes of Milton, Shakespeare, Oliver Cromwell and Isaac Newton – hardly barren years for this country!

Climatologists are hard at work now trying to discern what the overall trend is. Historical records point to one verdict, that some time in the 'near' future – near that is in terms of the history of the planet! – in 1,000 to 5,000 years time the next Ice Age will be upon us. However, a complicating factor is the so-called greenhouse effect, which may be leading to global warming, thereby postponing the next Ice Age. There are other factors to be taken into account too, such as the effect of volcanic and man-produced dust on the climate, and the impact of fluctuations within the sun and the importance of the Earth's magnetic field.

All of this makes it a daunting task forecasting what is likely to happen in the short to medium term. The only thing that can be said for sure is that no one knows for certain what is going to happen! Even the most advanced computers around are not able to give a definitive answer when there are so many variables and so much of the planet's climate is still imperfectly understood. That said, I will now move on to discuss some of these sources of potential climate change, beginning with the phenomenon that has hit the headlines over the last few years – the greenhouse effect.

Global Warming
The Greenhouse Effect

Everyone, it seems, it talking about the greenhouse effect. Never before has the subject of the climate featured so prominently in the news, in countless television and radio programmes and in newspaper articles. The very expression, the 'greenhouse effect' has entered the dictionaries and is now a widely used phrase. In addition, governments including our own via the Meteorological Office and other scientific bodies, are investing in studies to determine the extent and likely impact of the phenomenon. This recent concern is very necessary; if the worst fears about the many predictions on the greenhouse effect come true it will have a profound impact on human life. If not today's adults, then certainly our children and grandchildren will have to live with the legacy of such change. But I think that at the outset it is important to stress a few points about the greenhouse effect which are commonly overlooked in much of the media discussion, and which may help to put the matter into context.

First of all, the greenhouse effect is a natural process which existed long before man arrived on Earth and will doubtless continue to exist long after man has vanished from the planet. Moreover, without the formation of the greenhouse effect many millions of years ago there could have been no life on Earth; without it now man would not continue to live on the planet. The whole scientific debate surrounding the effect is not about how the greenhouse effect can be stopped, rather about how it may be slowed down. Or more succinctly, the fear is over the global warming caused by man-made adjustments to the Earth's greenhouse.

An Explanation

The greenhouse effect is a simple term used to explain how the Earth's atmosphere is able to keep the surface of the Earth warm while allowing a balance between the sun's heat energy coming in and the heat energy radiated out by the Earth. The energy of the sun coming into the Earth's atmosphere is short wave-length radiation – the visible radiation or sunlight that we see. One-third of this is reflected directly back into space by clouds and dust in the Earth's atmosphere. Of the remaining two-thirds, most reaches the Earth's surface and warms up the land and oceans. (However, less than 50 per cent is actually absorbed by the Earth's surface.) Meteorologists describe this by saying that the atmosphere is almost 'transparent' to the sun's rays. A small amount, though, is absorbed by the atmosphere and warms it slightly. Now we know from our own experience that if something is heated – for example a stone – it also then gives off or radiates heat. So it is with the Earth when heated by the sun's rays.

However, the radiation emitted by the surface of the Earth, which is much cooler than the sun, is of a much longer wave length and is entirely in the form of invisible infra-red radiation. It is some of this radiation, heading back up towards space, that is absorbed by atmospheric gases. This trapping of the Earth's heat is known as the greenhouse effect – it helps to warm up the surface of the planet. It might be wondered at this point why, according to this process, the whole Earth does not get warmer and warmer indefinitely. The answer is that eventually some of this heat does radiate back into space from the atmosphere itself. Also, and this will be crucial later in our discussions on the future impact of global warming, there is a limit to how much energy the Earth's atmosphere can absorb from the surface of the Earth. Eventually a maximum temperature will be reached. Thus the atmosphere acts like a kind of valve, regulating the crucial equilibrium between heat entering and leaving the planet.

The reason the greenhouse analogy is made is that the constructions we use to grow our tomatoes work in similar way to the atmosphere. The garden greenhouse allows the sun's rays in, but the panes of glass also stop some of the longer-wave, infra-red radiation from being radiated out from the inside of the greenhouse. The Earth's atmosphere can also be seen as a kind of blanket; if it did not trap the heat from the sun, the surface of the Earth where man lives would be too cold to support life.

What would the Earth be like without a greenhouse effect? It has been calculated that with no greenhouse gases in our atmosphere, the surface of the Earth would be around -19°C (-2.2°F), that is some 34°C (93.2°F) cooler than the current average and far too cold to support life. In contrast Venus, too, has a greenhouse effect but one which has 'got out of hand' and produced temperatures of up to 500°C (932°F), caused by a high atmospheric carbon dioxide content of 97 per cent – certainly a little warmer than even our most avid sun-lovers would want! The vital difference between the planets – and one which will ensure the Earth could not become like Venus – is the presence of the oceans here. Seventy per cent of the Earth's surface is made up of water and it is suspected that the oceans may work rather like a giant thermostat. For example, if the sun were to get hotter – and the energy output of the sun has changed during the 4.5 billion–year history of the planet – then this would heat the oceans, causing more water to be evaporated. This evaporation would form clouds, the upper surfaces of which would reflect the sunlight entering the atmosphere thereby reducing the impact of the increased heat from the sun. Alternatively, if the sun's energy output was to wane there would be less evaporation of the oceans and accordingly fewer clouds. The Earth would therefore receive greater benefit from the weaker sun. Although the final effect of the oceans is uncertain we must hope that they will save us from the fate of Venus. On that planet it is thought that there would have been much less water vapour to start with than on the Earth because it is closer to the sun. So, there were no oceans there to provide this 'thermostatic' balance and the planet just got warmer and warmer.

The Greenhouse Gases

So far I have talked generally about the 'atmosphere' and its role in the greenhouse effect. But the atmosphere is in fact made up of a number of different gases in varying quantities, some of which have little or no impact on global warming; while others have a very important effect. These are known now by the term 'the greenhouse gases'. By far the most abundant gas in the atmosphere is nitrogen which makes up some 78 per cent by volume, with oxygen, the gas we breathe, making up 21 per cent. Neither of these is a greenhouse gas, that is they do not absorb any of the infra-red radiation radiating from the Earth to any significant extent. Thus it can be seen that 99 per cent of the

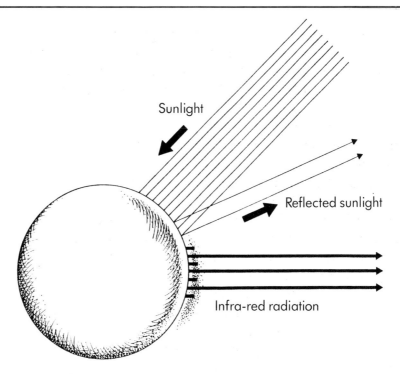

atmospheric gases in dry air are invisible to outgoing radiation; the greenhouse effect is caused by just one per cent or so of the atmosphere. The two most important of these gases are water vapour and carbon dioxide (CO_2). Water vapour content in air is variable but averages around 4 per cent. Carbon dioxide makes up some 0.03 per cent of the atmosphere – a figure which seems insignificant. Scientific evidence shows, however, that this is far from being the case.

There are other important greenhouse gases such as methane (CH_4), the chlorofluorocarbons (CFCs), nitrous oxide (N_2O), ozone (O_3). All these gases, in effect, make up the 'glass panes' in the terrestrial greenhouse – letting the short-wave sun radiation in but trapping the long-wave heat from the Earth

Relative contribution to the greenhouse effect of the various gases

Greenhouse gas	Appropriate relative greenhouse effect per molecule	Current (1988) average atmospheric concentration (ppmv)	Current rate of change (%p.a.)
CO_2	1	350	0.4
Methane	30	1.7	1
Nitrous Oxide	160	0.31	0.3
Ozone (lower atmosphere)	2,000	0.06	1.5
CFC 11	21,000	0.00026	5
CFC 12	25,000	0.00044	4

inside. However, they do not all trap and absorb this infra-red radiation in the same way. For example, a single molecule of CFC 12 (one of the chlorofluorocarbons) has about the same impact as around 25,000 molecules of carbon dioxide, while methane has some thirty times as great an effect. However, even though the amount of carbon dioxide in the atmosphere is small, it is much larger than the other gases. All of these gases, apart from the CFCs, occur naturally but the concern at the moment is about the increase in greenhouse gases from man-made sources. The worry is this: that if the amount of greenhouse gases in the atmosphere increases significantly then more heat will be trapped inside, causing the temperature to rise on the Earth – global warming. The chief concern surrounds carbon dioxide because of its importance as a greenhouse gas and also because of the vast amounts of it which are being pumped into the atmosphere by man each year.

The Carbon Question

There seems no doubt that the amount of carbon dioxide in the Earth's atmosphere has increased in very recent times. Before the start of the Industrial Revolution in the late 18th century it is estimated that there was about 280ppm of carbon dioxide present compared with the current rate of 350 parts per million (ppm). Since 1957 there have been accurate measurements of CO_2 levels carried out at Mauna Loa in Hawaii, a good site for such records as it is far away from large sources of pollution. Results indicate that the level of carbon dioxide is rising at about 0.4 per cent a year – a significant amount. Other studies estimate that man is responsible for adding a net amount of 3,000 million tons of carbon (as carbon dioxide) into the atmosphere each year. (To put this in perspective, I should point out that the atmosphere contains around 1,200 trillion tons of oxygen!) All in all current suggestions claim that the level of carbon dioxide in the atmosphere may be double that of pre-Industrial Revolution times by the middle of the next century. Moreover, when the projected increase of the other gases are taken into account, it is thought that the increase in greenhouse gases could reach the equivalent of a doubling of carbon dioxide between now and sometime in the 2020s.

Sources of Greenhouse Gases

Carbon dioxide has always existed naturally in the Earth's

atmosphere, as indeed it has in other planets. We have seen that Venus' atmosphere contains 97 per cent carbon dioxide; Mars' is also high, at 95 per cent. In the beginning the Earth, too, had a much larger amount of carbon dioxide in its atmosphere – pumped out from the core of the planet by volcanic activity. Gradually, however, as the Earth cooled down and the oceans and rain systems developed the carbon dioxide was dissolved into the seas and eventually formed vast sedimentary deposits. These rock deposits contain vastly more carbon than is in the atmosphere at present and although some of this is now being released as a by-product when lime is extracted from limestone for making cement, this is relatively insignificant in overall global terms. Forest and vegetation are other potential sources of carbon. Plant life absorbs atmospheric carbon dioxide during the photosynthesis process but this is then released again if, for example, a forest is cut down and burnt. Hence the importance of de-forestation as a source of carbon dioxide and the resulting international concern over the destruction of forests, particularly rain forests, in many parts of the world. According to recent figures the carbon dioxide released by de-forestation accounts for 20 per cent of the carbon dioxide which man causes to enter the atmosphere every year. This is in addition to the effect that removing the forests has on the local water cycle.

An even more important source for man-produced carbon dioxide is the burning of fossil fuels such as coal, oil and natural gas. It is estimated that some 22.5 per cent of man-produced CO_2 comes from cars and other vehicles burning up oil, while a similar amount is produced by the burning of fossil fuels at power stations to create electricity. It is these areas which cause some of the greatest concern in the debate on global warming. Man needs energy sources and while fossil fuels are finite resources and will run out one day, supplies of them are still vast (especially of coal) and will be used for many years to come. Until other sources of plentiful energy are developed, power stations will continue to pump out large amounts of carbon dioxide into the atmosphere. However, there is an important and often overlooked point here which does bring some comfort for those worried about the long-term future of the planet. The coal, gas and oil which we use are fossil fuels created by the build-up of vegetation hundreds of millions of years ago. The carbon contained in those plants, and hence the fossil fuels, must once have existed in the Earth's atmosphere (as carbon dioxide). So

following this logic, even if man burns all the fossil fuels in the Earth, he will not be putting into the atmosphere any more carbon dioxide than had once previously been in it. This is not to say there is no reason to worry about global warming, as we shall see, but it does mean that some of the more extreme forecasts of global destruction are put in their perspective; the Earth has seen it all before!

The release of methane into the atmosphere is caused by a variety of means, including farming, mining and the natural processes of the Earth. Evidence suggests that the amount of methane in the atmosphere has increased steadily since the early part of the last century with a more rapid rise of perhaps one per cent a year more recently. One of the reasons for this is that other human pollutants such as carbon dioxide actually slow down the rate at which methane is removed naturally from the atmosphere. Nitrous oxide, another greenhouse gas, is produced by plants but also, and this accounts for its recent increase, as a by-product of industry and agriculture. CFCs have been much in the news lately because of their impact on the ozone layer (I deal with this separately later). They are used as propellants in aerosols, and in fridges, and though only a very small amount exists in the atmosphere they are powerful greenhouses gases. The amount of CFCs in the atmosphere is increasing by up to four per cent a year, though recent international agreements to reduce and ultimately eliminate their use are hoped to have a significant impact but halofluorocarbons are also a potent greenhouse gas, albeit a bit less than CFCs. Ozone exists both high in the atmosphere, in the stratosphere where it filters out harmful ultraviolet rays, and also in the lower atmosphere, the troposphere, where it is a greenhouse gas. At this level it seems to have been increasing, probably due to industrial emissions of chemicals, but is still too rare to have a major effect compared with carbon dioxide or methane.

Global Warming – the Evidence

The existence of what is now known popularly as the greenhouse effect is not in doubt. Nor is there much doubt, as I have said above, that the global greenhouse is becoming 'thicker' as more and more greenhouse gases enter the atmosphere. The elements of uncertainty arise when we go on to

Rainforest destruction in Brazil.
M. Rautkari/WWF

149

consider the implications of what I have outlined. Essentially there are two key questions. First, is there evidence that the undoubted increased concentration of greenhouse gases is causing discernible global warming? Secondly, is it possible to predict what the likely rise in temperatures will be, given the forecasts for the emission of greenhouse gases in the future?

On the first point there is still some dispute. Historically the correlation between increased amounts of carbon dioxide in the atmosphere and global mean temperatures looks very strong. A graph showing both levels of carbon dioxide and mean temperatures over a period of some 160,000 years shows an almost identical pattern between the two; when CO_2 levels are higher, so is the temperature; if the levels are lower, so is the temperature. More recent history also points to the existence of some global warming.

In Britain we have experienced mild winters and hot summers and water shortages have become more commonplace. There is also evidence that temperatures have risen overall in the world by some 0.5°C (0.9°F) since the year 1860 and this trend appears to be continuing. Against that we must consider that there have, in the recent past, been small warming periods, such as the years 1910 to 1940, which then stabilized. Such spells of warming could be caused by more short-term factors and may not provide any evidence of overall global warming. Also, in the spring of 1990 scientists at the American space agency NASA and the University of Alabama published a report based on satellite observations of the 1980s which indicated no significant climatic trends – neither a net trend towards cooling nor warming. However, such studies are conducted over far too short a period to give any real guidance as to whether there is any overall climatic trend. Even within a warming climate there can be cool spells caused by the infinite natural variations and eccentricities of weather.

In general, then, most scientists would accept that there is some evidence of global warming. These tie in with the computer models used to 'forecast' future climatic developments.

The Computer Models

Detailed observations are useful in providing evidence for past or current global warming. But of course man needs to know what the likely extent of any such warming may be, and the past is of only limited value here. Instead scientists have to use their own version of the crystal ball, the computer projections.

The main method of predicting future changes is with 'general circulation models' or GCMs. These complex mathematical models are similar to the ones used in short-term weather forecasting and entail the use of powerful computers. The difference with the GCMs is that they are allowed to 'run' for years ahead. These experiments require massive computer resources. They are first tested by simulating the current climate before they are given different levels of greenhouse gases, for example a doubling of carbon dioxide, to see how the climate will alter under such circumstances. The results take some time to adjust and become stable; when they do, this is known as the 'equilibrium response'. At the moment there is no one figure which scientists using GCMs agree on, and predictions (based on an increase equivalent to doubling of CO_2) range from 2°C (3.6°F) to 5°C (9°F) warmer than those of the pre-industrial world – a considerable variation. One of the main inadequacies of the GCMs is that they fail to take full account of the effect of the oceans which perform a vital role in adjusting the temperature of the planet and moving heat around. However, taken as a whole the results do indicate that if the carbon dioxide levels rise as expected then there will be some significant global warming – and so far the computer predictions are consistent with the rises in temperature already observed.

The Imponderables

Why is it so difficult to predict accurately something so important as global warming?

One problem is in forecasting the level in carbon dioxide that will be present in the atmosphere. The predictions I have mentioned are based on the assumption that the level of greenhouse gases will be equivalent to a doubling of CO_2 by around 2020, as I said earlier. This assumption is as accurate as possible, based itself on the current output of carbon dioxide, the amount increasing in the atmosphere each year and the expected production of the gas, for example in electricity generation. But these figures are subject to change. Electricity generation using fossil fuels may soar or plummet depending on a whole host of scientific, social, political and economic issues. Just as important is the question of whether this extra carbon dioxide can be absorbed naturally. At the moment it appears that around half the 'extra' CO_2 being produced is absorbed, by vegetation and particularly by the oceans – the so-called carbon dioxide 'sinks'. No one yet knows whether this absorption rate will continue at the same pace (as assumed in the current predictions), or will speed up, or, more feasibly, slow down as natural absorbents become saturated. It is thought that within a thousand or so years the oceans would be able to absorb the extra carbon dioxide pumped into the atmosphere; though this may be a little too long for us to wait! The continuing destruction of the rain forests may also throw the calculations awry. Once the estimates for CO_2 levels are wrong, then the forecasts which use them as data will go wrong too.

There are other factors which also make such forecasts extremely difficult. It is often assumed that if the CO_2 levels are different from the original forecast, then the resulting temperatures will be proportionately different. This is to say, for example, that if a doubling of CO_2 produces a warming of 2°C (3.6°F), then one and a half as much CO_2 would produce a warming of 1°C (1.8°F). However, the elements of climate are so complex that this kind of assumption may well not be warranted, and such predictions become little more than educated guesses.

There are also what are known in the jargon as 'climatic feedback mechanisms'. These are a host of variable factors which could have an important bearing on the precise extent of any warming. One such is the presence of water vapour. Under the Met Office's own GCM the effect of doubling CO_2 itself would only increase temperatures by 1°C (1.8°F); however, their model takes into account the increased water vapour that a warmer atmosphere can contain which acts as a greenhouse gas and increases the temperature. The Met Office model also considers the reduced amount of ice and snow when temperatures rise. Ice and snow reflect solar energy, not absorb it. Less reflective surfaces means the earth will absorb more energy, and thereby cause the temperature to rise. All this adds up, says the model, to an overall warming from these effects of around 2°C (3.6°F).

Clouds too play an important role in trying to assess temperature changes. High clouds generally cause heating by trapping infra-red radiation coming from the Earth's surface, while low clouds tend to have the opposite effect by shielding the Earth from the sun's rays. So far most predictive models envisage an increased amount of high or medium cloud, which would increase the warming, perhaps up to 4°C (7.2°F). On the other hand, if there is more water vapour in the atmosphere, then the clouds lower down will be denser allowing less sunlight in. This would reduce the figure to below 4°C (7.2°F).

As we can see, then, the task of predicting just what the changes in temperatures will be, if any, is a formidable one. And working out just what the change will be over a particular part of the globe, for example the British Isles, is also very difficult. However, it is thought likely that because of the warming effect of melting snow and ice, as I describe above, the surface temperature in winter will rise more sharply towards the poles compared with the equator. (The enhanced warming near the poles is also a result of the low-level inversion in high latitudes in winter.) So while the overall temperature rise of the Earth may be around 2°C (3.6°F), it will not be in a uniform pattern. The effect will be more over high latitudes such as northern Europe, and considerably lower near the tropics. This theory is reflected also in the Met Office's own computer model.

Another factor to take into account is that the global warming will occur gradually over a number of years, rather than in an abrupt quantum leap. This gradual rise may well be partially disguised by the many other 'background' climatic influences which have an effect on the weather. It is likely that only with hindsight, in say twenty years time, will we know for sure that global warming, directly attributable to the increase in greenhouse gases, has occurred. It could be, of course, that we are merely going through a 'natural' period of global warming as the planet pulls out of the last Little Ice Age, a brief respite before the next main Ice Age. Conversely, any global warming may be counter-balanced by 'natural' global cooling. Moreover, there is a tendency on the part of some people to want to ascribe every unusual element of weather to the greenhouse trend – as if extremes of weather had never occurred before.

It is widely accepted that there is enough evidence now to convince most experts that we are already experiencing global warming and that this will become more apparent over the coming decades. Indeed scientists agree that we are bound to reap the harvest of the rise in greenhouse gases that has already occurred. The effect of the oceans has merely delayed this impact, which is known as 'unrealized' warming. Should temperatures rise by 2030 to 2°C (3.6°F) above pre-industrial levels this would mean a warming rate some ten times greater than previously experienced on Earth for a million years.

The Effects

If we consider the long history of the planet we can see how starkly climate and conditions on Earth have varied. During periods of great global warmth, millions of years ago, when dinosaurs walked the Earth luscious tropical-style vegetation covered what is now the British Isles. Much more recently, large parts of the British Isles were covered in glaciers from the Ice Age and the climate was cold and inhospitable. As the Ice Age receded the sea levels rose. Until about 10,000 years ago the British Isles had a land link with the rest of Europe, before the waters came and opened up the Straits of Dover. Climate is always changing; but now it seems we could be in for faster change than usual as a result of actual and projected global warming.

Sea Levels

One of the most talked-about changes is the expected rise in sea levels because of a leap in temperatures. Not surprisingly, most talk in the media has concentrated on the dramatic-sounding idea of the polar ice caps melting and pushing sea levels up many metres. In fact there is a very wide range of views among scientists about how much sea levels will rise. Recent estimates have been revised downwards, predicting a best estimate rise of 18 centimetres (7 inches) by 2030 and 58 centimetres (29 inches) by 2090. Around half of any rise would not be caused by melting ice but by what is called 'thermal expansion' of the oceans. That is to say, the increased heat energy in the seas would cause the volume of water to expand. The rest of the rise would be caused by the melting of glaciers and melting polar-land ice sheets. Sea ice, such as that on the frozen Arctic Ocean, does not enter the equation because it floats and displaces its own weight in the water anyway. The most likely area to find land ice melting is Greenland in the northern hemisphere. In the southern hemisphere, where predictions for climate change are even less precise, it is thought that snowfall could actually increase at the Antarctic. This is because increased global temperatures would create more water vapour in the atmosphere and more likelihood of clouds and snow developing. In any case the temperatures at the Antarctic are expected to stay well below freezing. Some scientists have predicted that the vast West Antarctic ice sheet could detach itself and melt, causing a huge rise in sea levels of up to 5 metres (16 feet). However, most people agree that the sheet is too firmly anchored to the icy continent for there to be any risk of that happening.

There is also the question of timing. The oceans take a long time to heat up so, although because of 'unrealized' global warming there will be some rises, these may take many years to come to fruition.

Any significant rises in sea levels naturally threaten low-lying

Areas of Great Britain vulnerable to a rising sea level.

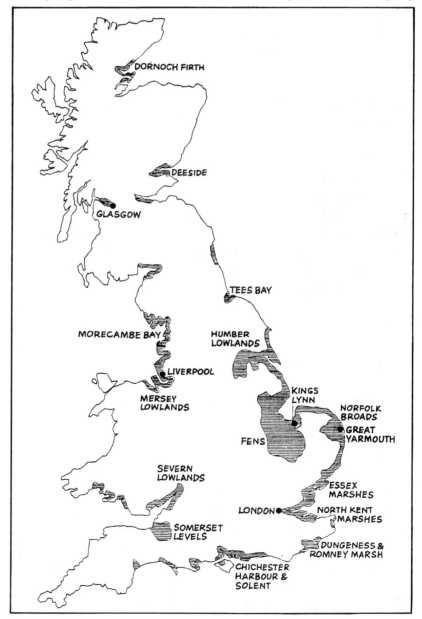

stretches of land, including many in the British Isles. Many of the world's capitals have been built at or very close to sea level, including London. The costs of protecting a country from the invading sea will be huge. In the British Isles it has been estimated that strengthening sea defences against a rise of around one metre would cost in the region of £5 billion! The vulnerable spots in Britain include the Thames estuary area and London, the Fens and the Norfolk Broads, the Somerset Levels, the Mersey Lowlands and the Solent area.

The effects of sea encroachment could be very large. Many areas of marshland could vanish, and with them large numbers of wildlife such as wading birds. The risk of flooding for many areas would increase and areas of land not long reclaimed from the sea would probably have to be surrendered back to the waters. It almost goes without saying that a number of fine sandy beaches could be lost. The potential problem has led to calls for a national initiative to take an overall look at coastal defences, instead of the piecemeal council-by-council approach that currently exists.

Climate

As I said earlier, no one knows for sure what the precise effect of global warming will be on any given area. But it has been predicted that the climate in the British Isles could change to the extent that it becomes similar to the present climate in the south-west of France; that is, hotter summers and milder winters. Perhaps our perpetual moaning about the weather would become a thing of the past! For naturally such a change would bring some advantages. Land could be cultivated at higher altitudes than at present, the types of crops that farmers grow would change, and sunflowers and maize corn might become regular features of the fields. Chickens and pigs, for example, would be cheaper to keep in warmer conditions which could lower food prices; beans, cabbages and cauliflowers would be cheaper and more plentiful. Perhaps olives could be cultivated here for the first time. Otters may flourish in the Highlands again. Home tourism would increase. But there would also be disadvantages, such as an increase in pests. And recalling recent problems with dry weather, drought could be a serious problem in some parts of the country. We would also have to adapt to different rainfall patterns, with its impact on rivers, irrigation and underground water supplies. And some have also blamed the presence of huge 'clouds' of algae on sea and lake surfaces on increased temperatures.

The Implications for Food

Inevitably a change in temperatures around the world will alter rainfall patterns. Much of the world's agriculture is highly sophisticated and geared to gaining maximum yields from the existing soil and weather conditions. A significant alteration in rainfall could drastically affect this. It has been estimated that rainfall would increase over areas such as India and the Middle East, which would be welcome relief indeed for such dry areas. But alarmingly it has also been predicted that huge agricultural areas such as the Soviet Union and the United States would receive less rain, which could seriously affect world grain production. Parts of the United States are known as the 'bread basket of the world' and it is from there that surplus grain for the Soviet Union and also the Third World comes. Any large failure of the crops could have a very dramatic effect on feeding the world's ever-growing population.

The Answers

There are no short-cut solutions to the problems of global warming. One approach is to cut down on the amount of greenhouse gases produced, though with the increasing demand on energy it is a difficult goal to achieve. In any case, though the increase of greenhouse gases may be contained there is an element of global warming to which we are already committed. This means that man must also learn to adapt to the changing climatic conditions to avoid any social or economic problems.

There is now widespread international co-operation and agreement on the need to do something about the threat of global warming. There is emphasis on searching for sources of energy which do not produce greenhouse gases or other pollutants; on making sure that prices charged for existing energy reflect the environmental cost of using such energy; and increasingly it is realized there must be some control on the amount of rain forest which is being destroyed, before it is too late.

The Ozone Layer

Much attention has recently been given to the problem of the depletion of the ozone layer. Ozone, which has the chemical symbol O_3, compared to oxygen which is O_2, exists in a layer in the Earth's stratosphere. (It also exists further down in the troposphere where it acts as a greenhouse gas, as I mentioned earlier.) Its main function here is to filter out the harmful short-wave, ultraviolet radiation from the sun. It is these rays which cause burning and can cause skin cancer. In the early 1970s scientists discovered that the man-made chlorofluorocarbons (CFC 11 and CFC 12) in the atmosphere – commonly used in aerosols as propellants, and in fridges and insulation – were depleting the ozone layer. (Incidentally, it is not strictly accurate to talk about 'holes' in the ozone layer so much as thinning of the layer.) By the mid 1980s it became apparent that with the level of CFCs increasing by about four per cent a year, this depletion of ozone was becoming very serious and that the levels of ultraviolet radiation piercing the atmosphere could increase as a result. Thus in 1987 there was an international agreement, known as the 'Montreal Protocol on Substances which Deplete the Ozone Layer' at which member states vowed to reduce and ultimately eliminate the use of CFCs. At an international environment conference in London in June 1990, signatories to the Protocol agreed to accelerate the timetable, with a 50 per cent cut in CFCs by 1995, an 85 per cent cut by 1997 and elimination by the year 2000. China and India, which between them account for 40 per cent of the world's population, also agreed to sign the Protocol at that conference. Some CFC substitutes now being developed will also deplete the ozone layer, but to a lesser extent – and agreement has also been reached to phase these out in the early part of the next century.

Conclusion

I hope that in this book I have given a taste of how varied and massive the subject of weather is – far beyond the weather forecasts we see on our television screens. And all the time the frontiers of our knowledge about weather are being constantly pushed back, with scientists coming up with new theories and new and more powerful computers putting those theories to the test.

On subjects such as global warming and the depletion of the ozone layer in particular the state of our knowledge is fast-changing, though most experts agree that both present severe challenges to the planet. Hopefully, current initiatives, including those at the Meteorological Office in Bracknell, will go a long way towards producing a clear picture of such issues.

But weather affects us at the local level too – showers that rain on summer fetes and off-shore breezes that cool us on hot sunny days. One thing I have tried to encourage is people observing the weather around them and using the signs of clouds and the winds to help forecast the weather themselves.

Weather is, after all, something from which we can never escape on this planet, whether we are experiencing the bitingly cold Antarctic, the searing heat of the Sahara, or a cold foggy day on the west coast of the British Isles. And without it, what on earth would the English ever find to talk about . . .?

Every effort has been made to correctly identify photographs. The publishers will be pleased to correct any errors and omissions in future editions.

Printed in the United Kingdom for HMSO
Dd 292880, C100, 9/90, 38938